Dictionary
of
Astronomy

BROCKHAMPTON PRESS
LONDON

This edition published 1995 by Brockhampton Press, a member of
the Hodder Headline PLC Group.

ISBN 1 86019 098 7

Printed and bound in Slovenia

A

Abell Catalogue a catalogue of clusters of GALAXIES.

aberration (1) (astronomical) the apparent displacement of a STAR from its true position caused by the finite VELOCITY OF LIGHT. In the time light from a star moves the length of a telescope the telescope moves with the earth, these motions add as VECTORS and the resultant appears to come from a star at a slightly displaced position. The effect is most obvious in observations at half-yearly intervals when the EARTH in its ORBIT round the SUN is moving in opposite directions in space. (2) (optical) one of the forms of IMAGE imperfection caused by an optical system; classes are: spherical, astigmatic, coma, distortion, field curvature, and by a lens only, chromatic.

ablation the erosion of a solid body. A METEORITE is ablated in passing at high velocity through the Earth's atmosphere. Friction with air molecules generates heat, melting the surface and leaving a trail of ions, a shooting star.

absolute magnitude the APPARENT MAGNITUDE a star would have if seen from a standard distance of 10 PARSECS.

absolute zero -273.15ºC, the temperature at which any body has its lowest possible energy. This temperature is defined as zero Kelvin, 0 K.

absorption decrease in the intensity of radiation by interaction with matter.

absorption coefficient the ratio (reduction in intensity)/

(incident intensity) for RADIATION passing through unit thickness of material. It is usually WAVELENGTH-dependent.

absorption nebula a NEBULA shown by its absorption of radiation from other sources rather than its own emissions.

absorption spectrum a bright CONTINUOUS SPECTRUM from a wideband source may be crossed by dark lines (from atoms), bands (from molecules), or edges (from solids) by ABSORPTION on passing through relatively cool matter. White light from the Sun has a spectrum crossed by numerous FRAUNHOFER LINES. The element HELIUM was first identified from these.

abundance (of the elements) the ratio of the number of atoms or ions of an element to the number of atoms or ions of hydrogen in the same volume. This abundance ratio varies from star to star, giving information about stellar formation and evolution (*see* STELLAR EVOLUTION). Variations in different parts of the UNIVERSE are important in COSMOLOGY.

acceleration the rate of change of velocity with time.

acceleration of gravity all MASSES allowed to drop freely near the surface of the EARTH are acted on by the force of GRAVITY and accelerate at a constant rate, approximated to 9.81 metres/(second)^2. The gravitational force, and thus the acceleration, near the MOON's surface has about $^1/_6$ of this value. It varies very widely for other CELESTIAL BODIES.

accretion capture of matter by a celestial object, largely by gravitation.

Achernar (Alpha Eridani) a STAR of the 1st MAGNITUDE, one of the brightest stars and the leading star in the southern CONSTELLATION. Eridanus.

achondrite a STONY METEORITE lacking CHONDRULES, similar to igneous rock of low silica content on EARTH. Only 4 per cent of known meteorites are achondrites.

achromatic lens a lens combination designed to overcome chromatic aberration over a particular wavelength range.

acoustic wave a wave motion in which compressions and rarefactions of the material through which the wave travels occur in the direction of travel. A sound wave.

Acrux (Alpha Crucis) a binary star of the first MAGNITUDE. It is the brightest in the CONSTELLATION Southern Cross.

active galactic nucleus *see* **Markarian galaxy**.

active optics *see* **optics**.

active region a widely used term which includes GAS CLOUDS, where STAR FORMATION occurs; a GALACTIC NUCLEUS with a BLACK HOLE causing copious energy output; and an area on the SUN giving rise to a FLARE.

Adhara (Epsilon Canis Majoris) a star in the constellation of the PLOUGH.

adiabatic change any change in physical state of a system without ENERGY exchange with its surroundings.

Adonis a small ASTEROID, with a mass about 5×10^{10} kg.

Adrastea a small rocky SATELLITE of JUPITER, diameter about 20 km and orbit about 129,000 km from the centre of the planet.

aeronomy the study of the physics and chemistry of EARTH'S upper ATMOSPHERE, including temperature and its distribution, density, chemical constituents and reactions.

Ae star *see* **spectral classification**.

Agena *see* **Beta Centauri**.

AGK (Astronomische Gesellschaft Katalog *or* AG Catalogue) a compilation of the positions of all STARS brighter than 9th MAGNITUDE. AGK1 covered the sky north of 18º south DECLINATION, published in 1912; AGK2, based on photographs, was published in 1951-58. AGK3, including the star's PROPER MOTION, was available from 1969.

Ahnighito meteorite a METEORITE found by the explorer Peary in 1897 at Cape York in West Greenland. The name means 'The Tent', and the 30 ton mass is now in the USA.

airglow a faint luminescence of Earth's upper atmosphere. It is emitted from the whole sky at all times, exhibits no marked structure and arises from 80km to 120km above the surface. Some is due to RECOMBINATION of MOLECULES or ATOMS undergoing DISSOCIATION by sunlight. Dayglow, twilight glow and night glow are recognized.

Airy disk the central spot in the DIFFRACTION pattern produced from a point source of light by a circular aperture. It is used in comparison of RESOLVING POWER. Named after Sir George Airy, 7th Astronomer Royal (1835-81).

albedo the reflective-power of a non-luminous CELESTIAL BODY. The MOON reflects about 7 per cent of incident sunlight, an albedo of 0.07.

Albireo (Beta Cygni) *see* **Cygnus**.

Alcor (80 Ursae Majoris) a faint star of magnitude 4 in the constellation of the Great Bear. The Arabic name means 'faint one'. It was used as a test of vision.

Aldebaran (Alpha Tauri) a STAR of the 1st MAGNITUDE, one of the 15 brightest stars. A RED GIANT, it is a VARIABLE STAR and may have a faint RED DWARF companion.

Alfvén's theory the Swedish astrophysicist Hannes Alfvén, Nobel Prizewinner in 1970, developed a theory of frozen-in-flux, in which a PLASMA can be considered trapped by MAGNETIC FIELD lines. It is important in the study of cosmic rays and other moving charged particles, and a mathematical simplification allows the complex spiral paths taken by such particles in magnetic fields to be analysed. The idea is fundamental to attempts to produce controlled NUCLEAR FUSION.

Algol (Beta Persei) the second-brightest STAR in the constellation PERSEUS. It was the first studied of a class of stars named after it, in which two stars rotating round a common centre of mass periodically eclipse each other as seen from Earth. The brighter component is a hot DWARF STAR; the fainter, which eclipses the brighter one every 2.87 days, is a cool SUBGIANT; the pair forming an ECLIPSING BINARY. The name Algol is used for a computer language.

Allende meteorite a METEORITE found in Mexico. It is estimated to have weighed about 2 tons and consisted of CARBONACEOUS CHONDRITES.

Almagest an astronomical and mathematical encyclopedia completed in about AD 140 by Ptolemy of Alexandria. It included a STAR CATALOGUE based on that of Hipparchus of about 129 BC, listing some thousand stars. It was used as the basis of all Arabic and European astronomy until the start of the 17th century. The name is a corruption of the Arabic phrase 'the greatest'.

almanac a collection of data such as positions and brightness of CELESTIAL OBJECTS for the year ahead, often published by observatories, e.g. the *Astronomical Almanac*.

Alpha the first letter of the Greek alphabet, often used in astronomy to indicate the first in a sequence, eg. the STAR ACHERNAR is also known as 'Alpha Eridani', denoting the brighter star, as visible from Earth, in the CONSTELLATION Eridanus. Similarly, ALGOL, also known as Beta Persei, is the second brightest star in the constellation Perseus. This system was introduced in 1603 by Johann Beyer and the letters are known as Bayer letters.

Alpha Centauri the brightest star, 1st magnitude, of the constellation CENTAURUS. It has three components; the two brighter stars, one rather similar to the SUN and the other somewhat more red, orbit each other with a period of 80 years; the third is a RED DWARF with a long orbital period. This third member is the Sun's nearest neighbour, 1.3 PARSECS distant (4.2 LIGHT YEARS), and is known as PROXIMA CENTAURI.

Alpha Geminorum *see* **Castor**.

Alpha Herculis *see* **Ras Algethi**.

Alpha Orionis *see* **Betelgeuse**.

alpha particle one of the earliest PARTICLES recognized in RADIOACTIVITY, it consists of a high speed doubly IONIZED helium ATOM, ie. the NUCLEUS only of two PROTONS and two neutrons. It leaves a thick trail of IONS behind as it travels through matter. The energy source of a STAR is believed to be from FUSION reactions some of which involve alpha particles. These NUCLEAR REACTIONS can only take place at high temperatures where the heat energy overcomes the mutual repulsion of the positive nuclei. *See also* CARBON CYCLE.

Alphard (ALPHA Hydrae) the brightest STAR, 2nd MAGNITUDE, of the CONSTELLATION HYDRA.

Alpha Regio *see* **Venus**.

Alphekka (ALPHA Corona Borealis) the brightest STAR, 2nd MAGNITUDE but variable, of the northern CONSTELLATION Corona Borealis.

Alpheratz (ALPHA Andremidae) the brightest STAR, 2nd MAGNITUDE, of the CONSTELLATION ANDROMEDA.

Alps mountains on the MOON. The lunar Alps are of similar height to those on EARTH but arose as the rim of an ancient impact CRATER and not by folding of the crust.

ALSEP (APOLLO Lunar Surface Experiments Package) a self-contained package of experimental apparatus left on the MOON by the Apollo astronauts. It continues to monitor and relay information to EARTH, e.g. the presence of moonquakes.

Altair (ALPHA Aquilae) the brightest STAR, 1st MAGNITUDE, of the CONSTELLATION AQUILA.

altazimuth mounting one form of two-axis TELESCOPE mounting. ROTATION about the ALTITUDE axis, which is a horizontal axle, lets the telescope sweep out in a vertical ARC, a semicircle over the observer's head. Rotation about the AZIMUTH axis, a vertical axle, swings the telescope around the HORIZON. Combining the two motions permits the instrument to point anywhere in the sky, determined by its altitude and azimuth angles. Every CELESTIAL OBJECT seen from EARTH has an APPARENT MOTION due to the complex movement of the EARTH through space, most importantly its SPIN and its ORBITED MOTION. To compensate for this apparent motion, both altitude and azimuth angles require continuous alteration. The altazimuth mounting is frequently power-driven under computer control. The other common system, EQUATORIAL MOUNTING, can usually work with only one power-driven axis and may be simpler to use.

altazimuth system a system of coordinates to locate the position of a CELESTIAL OBJECT on the CELESTIAL SPHERE. (*See also* ALTITUDE, AZIMUTH, ALTAZIMUTH MOUNTING, ANGULAR MEASURE).

altitude the height of an object above a surface. In astronomy, using the ALTAZIMUTH SYSTEM, the altitude is the angle measured from the HORIZON upwards to the object. In this system vertically overhead is referred to as the ZENITH and has an altitude of 90° (AZIMUTH). *See also* ANGULAR MEASURE.

altimetry any measurement of the height of an object above some reference level.

Amalthea a SATELLITE of JUPITER discovered in 1892. An irregularly shaped object of average diameter 200 km, probably rocky but with a coating, perhaps of sulphur compounds from Io, giving a reddish colour. It has an ALBEDO of 0.06 and an ORBIT of about 181,000 km radius.

AM Herculis stars a class of STAR showing regular change in both BRIGHTNESS and POLARIZATION of light, sometimes called polars. They can be detected by X-RAY ASTRONOMY, having a source of SYNCHROTRON RADIATION rotating with the star and indicating the presence of MAGNETIC FIELD.

Amor an ASTEROID which was discovered in 1932 of diameter about 1 km. It is in an ECCENTRIC ORBIT with an INCLINATION of over 11° to the plane of the ECLIPTIC and comes close to the EARTH'S ORBIT, having a PERIHELION distance of 1.09 AU.

amplitude the maximum value of any regularly varying quantity during one PERIOD, eg in a simple pendulum the amplitude is taken as the angle the suspension moves through as the suspended mass rises from its lowest position to its highest in its swing. The term is also used more loosely to refer to the size or quantity of any thing.

Am stars *see* **spectral classification**.

Andromeda a northern sky CONSTELLATION, 1 hour RIGHT ASCENSION, 40°N DECLINATION. The brightest stars are of 2nd MAGNITUDE. ALPHA Andromeda is also known as ALPHERATZ or Sirrah. Contains the ANDROMEDA GALAXY. NGC24 or M31.

Andromeda galaxy a SPIRAL GALAXY found in the CONSTELLATION ANDROMEDA, referred to as NGC24 or M31. It is visible to the unaided eye and was the first STAR system shown to be outside our own MILKY WAY GALAXY, although at 700,000 PARSECS distant it is relatively close, and thought to be a member of the LOCAL GROUP of galaxies. It has a bright central NUCLEUS surrounded by spiral arms coiling round in the GALACTIC PLANE, both regions are filled with stars, HYDROGEN gas and dust. There are two smaller companion systems, NGC 205 and NGC221, and an almost spherical halo of GLOBULAR CLUSTERS. Although it has a diameter of 60,000 PARSECS and is roughly twice the size, it forms a model for the study of the Milky Way Galaxy.

Anglo-Australian Observatory a jointly funded OBSERVATORY situated on a mountain top at Siding Spring, about 300 km north of Canberra. As well as the ANGLO-AUSTRALIAN TELESCOPE, there is a 1.2m SCHMIDT TELESCOPE and a 2.3m advanced technology instrument with an ALTAZIMUTH mounting under computer control.

Anglo-Australian Telescope a 3.9m diameter TELESCOPE in operation since 1975 with particularly well-formed optical and guidance systems.

angström a size unit, 10^{10}m, originally used for measurement of optical WAVELENGTHS, now largely displaced by the vanometre, 10^{-9}m.

angular measure is used in the mathematical measurement of astronomical distances. A circle, centre C, radius r, has two radii, CA and CB, cutting off an ARC of length S, also the angle θ; θ is 'subtended by' or 'standing on' the arc S or the line AB. θ can be measured in RADIANS, θ = s/r; or in degrees, minutes and seconds (1 degree = 60 minutes, 1 minute = 60 seconds). The complete turn from CA round the circle to CA again is 2π radians, or 360°; thus θ is a fraction of 2π or 360°. For CA perpendicular to CB, S is $^1/_4$ of the circumference of the circle and θ = $\pi/2$ or 90°; for θ = π radians or 180° ACB is a straight line (the diameter) and the arc S is $^1/_4$ the circumference. Distances can be measured by triangulation from the properties of triangles like ABC.

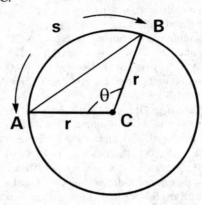

If two observatories at P and Q on EARTH direct TELESCOPES at a distant object, O; the angles, α and β, to the local vertical are measured, thus γ is calculated, where γ is the angle of PARALLAX. Knowing the base line PQ and the parallax angle γ, all sizes of triangle POQ can be found and hence the distance from the CELESTIAL OBJECT O to the centre of the Earth E calculated. Even when the base line PQ is as large as possible (the diameter of Earth) the parallax angle γ is very small, and a very distant object gives γ too small to be measured. An extension of the method allows the diameter of the Earth's orbit to be used as a base line. As shown in the diagram opposite, an observatory makes two position angle measurements six MONTHS apart, i.e. using the diameter of Earth's orbit as base line and allowing much greater distances to be measured. The distance the Solar System moves in space in a year can also be used. This is known as secular parallax.

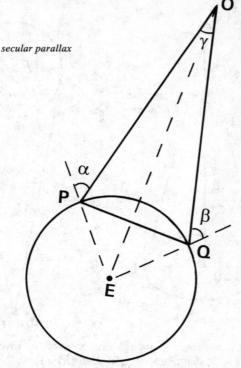

secular parallax

The usual unit of distance in astronomy is the PARSEC, defined by using the triangulation method, as shown in the diagram on page 18. One parsec is the distance at which a celestial object would be if it subtended an angle of 1 second of arc when measured over a base line of the radius of the Earth's orbit, i.e., 1 astronomical unit or au. 1 parsec = 206,265 au = 3.086×10^{13} km.

triangulation method in reverse

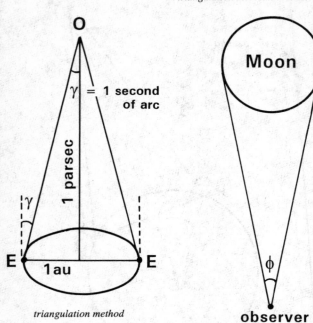

triangulation method

observer

The triangulation method can be used in reverse, as shown in the diagram above. An observer on Earth looking at the Moon can see that the diameter subtends an angle ø. If the diameter is known, then the Earth/Moon distance can be worked out, or vice versa. For both Sun and Moon, by coincidence, the angle ø is about $1/2°$. Although they have very different diameters they are at very different distances, thus the Moon can on occasion completely cover the Sun, giving the total ECLIPSE of the Sun.

angular momentum a VECTOR property characteristic of the rotatory motion of a body around an AXIS and the product of the ANGULAR VELOCITY and MOMENT OF INERTIA. It is conserved, i.e. keeps a constant value, unless changed by outside forces. The Earth has angular momentum from spin about its own axis and also from movement in orbit round the Sun. Both remain largely constant, changing only very slowly due to external influences.

angular velocity, symbol ω, is a measure of the rate of rotation of a body and the units are RADIANS/SECOND.

annual parallax due to PARALLAX, stars near the Earth appear to move against the background of distant stars, the FIXED STARS. As the Earth orbits the Sun, the maximum displacement occurs at half-yearly intervals (*See also* APPARENT MOTION).

anomalistic month the interval of 27.555 days between two successive passages of the Moon in its orbit round the Earth through PERIGEE.

anomalistic year the interval of 365.26 MEAN SOLAR DAYS between two successive passages of the Sun in its APPARENT MOTION through PERIGEE.

anomaly (1) one of three angles used in describing the ORBIT of a body in an ELLIPSE. (2) More loosely, the word is used to describe any deviation from the usual or predicted.

Antares (Alpha Scorpii) a variable binary star of the 1st MAGNITUDE, and the brightest in the CONSTELLATION SCORPIUS. The larger component is a red SUPERGIANT with a diameter of about 10^9 km; the smaller is a hot star of the 5th MAGNITUDE, and they ORBIT each other in about 900 years.

antenna the radiating or receiving component of a RADIO system, an aerial. *See also* ARRAY.

anthropic principle the idea that for the UNIVERSE to take the form it has and thus provide a home for intelligent life to evolve, there is very little latitude possible in the values of many FUNDAMENTAL CONSTANTS. 'The universe is as it is because if it were different we wouldn't be here to observe it'. (*Hawking*).

antimatter the material of the universe is composed of matter built up from an apparently small number of FUNDAMENTAL PARTICLES (e.g., a proton and an electron form a hydrogen atom). For each particle there would seem to be an anti-particle, which could perhaps form antimatter (e.g., an antiproton and a POSITRON could form an atom of anti-hydrogen). Most steps in this process have been observed but not isolated in bulk, for a particle encountering its anti-particle results in mutual annihilation with the masses converted to energy. This is an application of Einstein's mass-energy relation. *See also* ATOM; BETA DECAY.

Apennines mountains on the Moon.

aperture the maximum diameter of a light beam which can pass through an optical system, usually determined in a telescope by the diameter of the principal mirror or lens. The larger the aperture, the greater the light-gathering power of the instrument, enabling fainter objects to be seen, and also the greater the RESOLVING POWER, enabling finer detail to be studied.

aperture synthesis a technique used chiefly in RADIO ASTRONOMY to obtain the higher RESOLVING POWER of a large APERTURE by using small aerials separated by large distances. The method uses the aerials as an INTERFEROMETER.

apex the point on the CELESTIAL SPHERE towards which the Sun, and thus the Solar System, is moving. It is located by finding the PROPER MOTION and radial velocity of a sample of the stars in the Sun's neighbourhood and currently lies in the constellation HERCULES.

aphelion the point most distant from the Sun reached by any body in an elliptical ORBIT round the Sun. *See also* APSE; PERIHELION.

apoapse *see* APSE

apogee the point most distant from the Earth reached by any body in an elliptical ORBIT round the Earth. *See also* PERIGEE; APSE.

Apollo (1) an ASTEROID, found in 1932, which is irregularly shaped with a mean diameter of 1.4 km. It was the first found whose ORBIT crosses that of the EARTH, and it has come as close as 4.5×10^6 km. (2) The name was also used for the American Moon-landing project.

apparent a descriptive word given to a measurement where full allowance has not been made for all factors capable of influencing the observation, e.g. two STARS might appear to have the same BRIGHTNESS where one was in fact emitting much more light but was much further away.

apparent luminosity the LUMINOSITY of a celestial object as it appears from Earth. No allowance is made for reduction in brightness by light ABSORPTION in the INTERSTELLAR MEDIUM nor by the INVERSE SQUARE LAW of distance.

apparent magnitude the MAGNITUDE of a STAR as it appears from Earth. No allowance is made for reductions in brightness by light ABSORPTION in the INTERSTELLAR MEDIUM nor by the INVERSE SQUARE LAW of distance. *See also* ABSOLUTE MAGNITUDE.

apparent motion many celestial objects appear to move against the background of the FIXED STARS when viewed from Earth. This apparent motion is due to the motion of the Earth, principally its spin on its own axis and its movement in its elliptical orbit round the Sun. The Sun has a daily apparent motion, rising in the east, moving in an ARC through the sky and setting in the west, which reflects the spin of the Earth. Similarly, nearer stars appear to trace out small ellipses against the background of very distant stars as the Earth moves round the Sun once a year in its elliptical orbit. *See also* ANNUAL PARALLAX; PROPER MOTION.

apse, apse line a point or points located on an elliptic orbit. Any body in constant motion round a second very massive body to which it is attracted only by GRAVITY will in general have an orbit in the shape of an ellipse with the massive second body at one of the two symmetrically placed foci (*see* FOCUS). A line drawn between the foci and extended to cut the orbit (the major axis of the ellipse) does so at two points, called the *apses*. The *periapse* is that where the orbiting body is closest to the massive body; the *apoapse* that where it is farthest. The major axis may be called the *apse line* or the *line of apsides*. In the particular case of the Moon orbiting the Earth, the apse points are referred to as the PERIGEE and APOGEE for the nearer and further distances between the Moon and the Earth. These names are derived from the Greek word 'ge' for Earth. Similarly, in the Earth's orbit of the Sun, the nearest approach is referred to as the PERIHELION, and the furthest as APHELION.

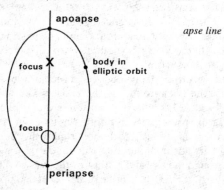

Ap star *see* **spectral classification**.

Aquarids METEOR SHOWERS to be seen in late April-early May, associated with HALLEY'S COMET and having a RADIANT in the constellation AQUARIUS.

Aquarius a zodiacal CONSTELLATION between CAPRICORN and PISCES at 23 hours RIGHT ASCENSION, $10°$ south DECLINATION. The brightest stars are of 3rd magnitude. It contains several features of interest: the GLOBULAR CLUSTER M2 or NGC 7089, which may be seen through binoculars; and two planetary NEBULAE, NGC 7009, known as the Saturn Nebula, and NGC 7293, known as the Helix Nebula.

Aquila an EQUATORIAL CONSTELLATION. The brightest star is the 1st magnitude Alpha Aquilae, also known as Altair. It lies in a populous region of the Milky Way Galaxy.

arachnoids spider shaped patterns of cracks of volcanic origin on VENUS.

arc a curved line, usually a portion of a circle. It is the basis of RADIAN measure and ANGULAR MEASURE.

Archer *see* **Sagittarius**.

Arcturus (Alpha Boötis) a star of the 1st magnitude in the constellation Boötes. It is a RED GIANT star with a large PROPER MOTION.

Arecibo Observatory an OBSERVATORY in Puerto Rico, 16 km south of Arecibo town, with the world's most powerful single-dish RADIO TELESCOPE. It was built in the 1960s, and the 305m dish, mounted in an extinct volcano crater, cannot be steered. Instead, as the Earth spins the dish surveys a circle in the CELESTIAL SPHERE, and this is broadened to a 40°-wide band by moving the receivers off axis. It receives radio signals from a wide variety of sources, but can also be used in active mode to transmit and receive radar impulses with which studies are made of Earth's atmosphere, asteroids and planets, in particular building up a detailed RADAR MAP of the surface of VENUS. It has also been used in a search for extraterrestrial intelligence.

Arend-Roland comet a COMET whose NUCLEUS reached 1st MAGNITUDE in 1957. It has a particularly impressive dust and gas TAIL, but an ANOMALY of a spike pointing towards the SUN proved to be an optical illusion.

areography the name given to the geography of MARS.

Argo Navis an anciently recognized CONSTELLATION but now split into three. Its brightest star was the 1st magnitude CANOPUS.

Ariane the name give to the ESA (European Space Agency) rocket-launching vehicle. The 71st firing occurred in March 1995.

Ariel (1) one of the five major satellites of URANUS, discovered in 1851. It is about 1200 km in diameter and appears to be largely made from water-ice, some methane and some rock. It has a complex surface with cratered regions broken up by cracks and faults. It is in a nearly circular orbit of radius 191,000 km. (2) The name is also used for the first international co-operative earth SATELLITE, launched in 1962.

Aries a zodiacal constellation lying between PISCES and TAURUS at 3 hours RIGHT ASCENSION and 20° north DECLINATION. It has no very bright stars. Alpha Arietis, also known as HAMAL, is of 2nd magnitude.

Arizona meteorite crater a 150m deep circular depression of diameter 1.2 km and with raised edges. It lies in the Arizona desert and was formed some 40,000 years ago by the impact of a metallic METEORITE estimated to be 25m diameter and of mass 65 tons.

array a regularly spaced group of aerials for RADIO ASTRONOMY. The array can collect a bigger proportion of the radio signals from a faint RADIO SOURCE and can also be used as a radio INTERFEROMETER to examine fine detail. *See also* RESOLVING POWER; BEAM WIDTH).

ashen light a faint illumination sometimes seen in the unlit side of VENUS. It may be analogous to AIRGLOW on Earth.

aspect *see* **phase**.

association a loose form of STAR CLUSTER.

A star *see* **spectral classification**.

asterism a chance grouping of stars forming a distinctive pattern, usually forming part of a CONSTELLATION.

asteroid any one of a large number (10^8) of small rocky bodies in solar orbits lying between MARS and JUPITER. Generally the orbits are nearly circular and lie close to the plane of the ECLIPTIC; a few cross the Earth's orbit. CERES was the first located, in 1801, and over 3000 are now listed. Ceres, PALLAS and Vesta have radii greater than 300 km. Those smaller than 120 km are often irregular in shape. Groups occur. HIRAYAMA FAMILIES, with similar orbits, are perhaps evidence for the break-up of a larger body. *C-type asteroids* are blue with featureless SPECTRA like CARBONACEOUS CHONDRITE METEORITES. *S-type asteroids* are reddish with spectra similar to STONY-IRON METEORITES. *M-type* have metallic spectra, and *U-type asteroids* are unclassified.

astigmatism an IMAGE imperfection in an optical system. Instead of a point image for a STAR, two short lines at right angles to each other are formed at slightly different distances along the AXIS.

astrobleme the remains of an ancient METEORITE impact on the Earth's surface, generally appearing as a circular scar and identified by 'shatter cones' in the bedrock beneath, with a distinctive radiating pattern. The word is from the Greek and means 'star wound'.

astrograph a TELESCOPE designed for accurate photography of the sky. The relative positions of stars can be measured to a high degree of precision and PROPER MOTION determined.

astrolabe an early instrument for reckoning time and for other observational purposes.

astrometry accurate measurement of the positions of stars and other objects on the CELESTIAL SPHERE. Two coordinates are used, DECLINATION and RIGHT ASCENSION, corresponding to latitude and longitude.

Astronomer Royal an honorary title given to an eminent British astronomer. The first appointment was made by Charles II in 1675, who established Flamsted in the post of director of the Royal Greenwich Observatory and Astronomer Royal. The two positions were held simultaneously until 1971 by which time the Observatory had been moved to Herstmonceux. The present Astronomer Royal, Arnold Wolfendale, is the fourteenth.

astronomical unit (abbreviated to **au**) the mean distance of the Earth from the Sun; 149,600,000 km forms the basis of astronomical distance measurements. The orbits of the planets in the Solar System are often expressed as multiples or fractions of the Earth's orbital radius, and the common astronomical distance measurement, the parsec, is based on it. *See also* ANGULAR MEASURE.

astronomy (from a Greek word originally meaning 'star-arranging') the science has grown to become the detailed study by all possible means of all CELESTIAL OBJECTS and of anything in the UNIVERSE beyond our own Earth. The objects studied include METEORITES, ASTEROIDS, COMETS, PLANETS and their MOONS, the SUN, other STARS and their ASSOCIATIONS, GALAXIES and CLUSTERS of galaxies, and also less clearly defined objects such as NEBULAE, GAS CLOUDS, and even DUST GRAINS. The study also includes objects that can never be seen, only inferred from their influences, like SUB-ATOMIC PARTICLES and BLACK HOLES.

Atlas (1) a small, 20 x 40 km satellite of SATURN. It is in a circular orbit of radius 137,670 km and completes one revolution in 0.6 days. It is a SHEPHERD SATELLITE. (2) A *star atlas* is a CATALOGUE recording positions of stars. (3) Atlas rockets were used as launch vehicles for space research.

atmosphere the gaseous envelope surrounding a CELESTIAL BODY. Earth's atmosphere is 78 per cent nitrogen, 21 per cent oxygen and small quantities of argon, carbon dioxide, water vapour, etc. The atmosphere is retained by gravitational attraction, so most massive celestial objects have an atmosphere, although the composition differs from planet to planet and star to star. Bodies of smaller mass—METEORITES, ASTEROIDS and most MOONS—have insufficient gravitational attraction to retain a permanent atmosphere. Gases present at their original formation or subsequently released from the interior through the crust gradually leak away into space as the ESCAPE VELOCITY is too low. COMETS coming close to the Sun have a temporary atmosphere as solar energy vaporizes some of the solid body (the HEAD or NUCLEUS) of the comet, giving rise to the HALO and TAIL of the comet. The tail streams away from the head, moving away from the Sun, carried by the SOLAR WIND.

atmospheric window a region in the ELECTROMAGNETIC spectrum to which Earth's atmosphere is transparent. The gases in the Earth's atmosphere, particularly water vapour, carbon dioxide and OZONE, have high ABSORPTION COEFFICIENTS for much of the CONTINUOUS SPECTRUM and give an ABSORPTION SPECTRUM, especially in the ULTRA-VIOLET and INFRA-RED. IONIZED LAYERS formed in the upper atmosphere by the absorption of solar energy also absorb or reflect RADIO WAVES. Observations can thus be made only in the gaps where absorption does not take place. Orbiting laboratories above the atmosphere avoid the absorption.

atom the smallest block of ordinary matter. An atom has a minute NUCLEUS, containing most of the mass and composed of uncharged NEUTRONS and positively charged PROTONS, and a surrounding cloud of very low mass, negatively charged ELECTRONS. The number of electrons is the same as the number of protons, so the atom is electrically neutral. Every atom of any one ELEMENT has an unique number of electrons, and thus protons, which determine its chemical properties, but it can have different numbers of neutrons, giving rise to ISOTOPES. There are 92 naturally occurring elements arranged in order in the PERIODIC TABLE, starting with 1 proton for hydrogen to 92 for uranium. A few are unstable, emitting one of the radioactive PARTICLES: α (alpha), a high-speed HELIUM nucleus; β (beta), a high-speed electron; and/or γ (gamma), a high-energy, short-wavelength, electromagnetic wave. The first two result in the atom being transmuted into a different element. Transuranic elements can be made artificially by bombarding natural elements in a nuclear reactor. All are unstable and DECAY more or less rapidly to one of the 92 natural elements.

It is found that the total mass of the nucleus of a light element (any one lower in the periodic table than iron, which has 26 protons) is very slightly less than the sum of the masses of the neutrons that form it. This discrepancy is known as the *mass defect*. Einstein's MASS-ENERGY RELATIONSHIP, $E = mc^2$ (where c is the velocity of light and E is the energy released when a mass m is converted to energy) shows that the mass defect represents both the energy that builds the nucleus and the energy released when it was formed by fusing neutrons together. It is believed that such fusion reactions, chiefly the 'burning' of hydrogen to helium, made possible by the very high temperatures and extreme pressures in a STAR's central regions are the main source of stellar energy. *See also* ANTIMATTER; BETA DECAY; CARBON CYCLE; PROTON-PROTON CHAIN.

atomic clock a device for measuring time where the mechanically oscillating mass of an ordinary timepiece is replaced by a much more constant atomic vibration.

au abbreviation of ASTRONOMICAL UNIT.

Auriga a northern sky CONSTELLATION. Its brightest star is CAPELLA (Alpha Aurigae) of 1st magnitude. Three STAR CLUSTERS, M36, M37 and M38, lie in the constellation.

aurora light appearing in curtains, arcs or bands, and often coloured, in the upper atmosphere (100 km) of EARTH. They most commonly occur in north polar latitudes (*Aurora Borealis*) and south polar latitudes (*Aurora Australis*). They are caused by upper-atmosphere atoms being hit by fast-moving charged particles from the Sun, these incoming particles being directed by the Earth's magnetic field.

axis a straight line, usually imaginary, indicating a direction of particular symmetry or importance. The axis of the Earth runs from pole to pole through the centre and can be thought of as the axle about which it spins. The axis of a telescope indicates the direction in which it points and round which lenses and mirrors are usually symmetrical.

azimuth one of the two angular measures in the ALTAZIMUTH SYSTEM used to locate the position of an object on the CELESTIAL SPHERE, the other being altitude. *See also* ALTAZIMUTH MOUNTING.

B

Baily's beads an arc of bright spots round the edge of the Moon seen during a total ECLIPSE of the Sun. The appearance is due to irregularities—mountains and valleys—on the edge of the MOON's dish, partially covering the bright PHOTOSPHERE at the LIMB of the Sun.

band spectrum a SPECTRUM, either ABSORPTION or EMISSION, where the principal features are broad bands of darkness or brightness usually with one sharp edge. Higher RESOLUTION shows the presence of many closely spaced LINES. Band spectra are due to MOLECULES.

bandwidth a section of a SPECTRUM between two well-defined WAVELENGTHS or FREQUENCIES. A radio receiver has a bandwidth narrow enough so that it can be tuned to a given transmission and be free from interference from neighbouring transmitters.

bar (1) a unit of pressure, one bar is 10^5 Newton m^{-2} and is roughly the normal pressure of the atmosphere on Earth. More frequently the millibar, 10^{-3} bar, is quoted. (2) Certain types of GALAXY are recognized where a bar cuts across the centre of the nucleus, these are known as *barred spirals*.

Barnard's star a dim 10th-magnitude star, about 2 PARSEC from the Solar System and having the largest PROPER MOTION known, 10 arc seconds/year (*see* ANGULAR MEASURE). It is a BINARY STAR, and irregularity in its motion may indicate the presence of one or more planets.

barycentre the common centre of mass round which the stars in a binary star system rotate. Two or more massive objects within each other's gravitational field orbit round each other, the effect being as if each was in orbit around the CENTRE OF MASS of the system.

baryons subatomic particles believed to be composed of QUARKS, so exhibiting strong nuclear forces. Protons and neutrons are examples.

basin a surface feature of planets and moons; a shallow, circular depression. MERCURY shows the Caloris Basin, about 1300 km in diameter, with a floor disrupted by ridges and surrounded by mountains up to 2km high. This is in many respects similar to the MARE of the Moon and is thought to have originated in the collision with a body of considerable mass. Basins are also found on VENUS.

barred spiral galaxy *see* **bar; galaxy**.

Bayer letters *see* **Alpha; Beta**.

beam width the distance or area between the edge rays of a beam of radiation. In telescopes and cameras it is often possible to improve the RESOLUTION of the IMAGE by narrowing the beam width.

Becklin-Neugebauer object a powerful source of infrared radiation in the ORION NEBULA. It may be due to a collapsing PROTOSTAR.

Becrux (Beta Crucis) a star of the 1st MAGNITUDE, the second brightest in the CONSTELLATION of the Southern Cross. It is a hot, variable giant star and along with ACRUX and ANTARES is a member of the Scorpius-Centaurus stellar ASSOCIATION.

Belinda a satellite of URANUS, about 50km in diameter and in a circular orbit of about 75,000 km radius.

Belt of Orion a distinctive feature of three visible stars across the middle of the CONSTELLATION ORION.

Be star *see* **spectral classification**.

Beta the second letter of the Greek alphabet, β, used in the BAYER LETTERS to distinguish the second brightest star in a CONSTELLATION.

Beta Centauri a bright giant star of 1st magnitude, the second brightest star in the CONSTELLATION CENTAURUS, also known as Agena or Hadar.

Beta Cephei Star a variable star, named after the first studied of the class, Beta Cephei, the second brightest star in the CONSTELLATION CEPHEUS. The origin of their variability of light output is less clearly understood than that of Delta Cephei, the important class of CEPHEID VARIABLES.

beta decay one form of natural RADIOACTIVITY where an unstable nucleus spontaneously emits a BETA PARTICLE, a high-speed electron, converting a neutron to a proton and forming a new element one place higher in the PERIODIC TABLE. A similar process occurs in which a positive electron or POSITRON is emitted and a PROTON converted to a NEUTRON.

In every beta decay process another PARTICLE, a NEUTRINO, is produced. It has spin, no charge, very low, if any, REST mass, and is thus extremely difficult to detect. (*See also* ATOM).

Beta Lyrae a STAR of 3rd magnitude, it is the second brightest in the constellation LYRA. An early discovered ECLIPSING BINARY star which has given its name to a class of stars, BETA LYRAE STARS.

Beta Lyrae stars a class of ECLIPSING BINARY where in addition to brightness variation produced by ECLIPSES, there are variations in the light output of the individual stars. It typically consists of two close components which are greatly distorted by mutual gravity, sharing a common atmosphere and exchanging matter from one component to the other.

beta particle *see* **beta decay**.

Beta Regio *see* **Venus**.

Betelgeuse (Alpha Orionis) a star of 1st magnitude, the brightest star in the constellation Orion. It is a red supergiant, semi-regular variable star. Attempts to measure its diameter by interferometry have given a value of 1.9×10^9 km, but as the star's distance from Earth is not known with any certainty, this diameter, greater than the ORBIT of JUPITER, is uncertain.

Bianca a small satellite of Uranus, about 50 km in diameter and in a circular orbit of radius 59,000 km.

Big Bang theory in cosmology, currently the most generally supported theory for the origin and evolution of the universe. The theory is that all radiation and matter were originally trapped in one compact region in the most highly condensed state—not even atoms existed, only their component particles crushed together. BLACK HOLES may reflect this highly compacted form. Some 15 thousand million years ago instability set in, and in the Big Bang the condensation exploded to form a PRIMEVAL FIREBALL, releasing radiation and hurling matter radially outward at very high velocity. The fireball cooled and for a brief time the temperature was suitable for NUCLEOSYNTHESIS. Nuclei of a limited range of the lightest elements were formed from the primordial matter. This material, now principally hydrogen gas with some helium and a few other light elements, continued to stream away from the centre, but eddies allowed local gravitational effects to form separate, enormous gas clouds. Due to their own gravity the massive clouds sucked in neighbouring gas and began to contract. Similarly, eddies within any one cloud allowed more localized gravitational ACCRETIONS to form. In both cases the gas cloud suffered gravitational collapse and became heated by ADIABATIC contraction, which continued until the temperature at the core of the smaller bodies rose high enough for nucleosynthesis to start up again in the form of nuclear fusion reactions converting hydrogen to helium. The energy released stabilized the body, just balancing the gravitational collapse and releasing radiant energy. A star was born. On this scale the smaller eddies became stars or STAR CLUSTERS, whilst the massive clouds became GALAXIES and CLUSTERS OF GALAXIES. The expanding universe continued on the still larger scale, however. Thus the galaxies all appear to be rushing away from each other with velocities proportional to their separations, whilst the BLACK BODY radiation expanding from the primeval fireball forms the MICROWAVE BACKGROUND RADIATION, at 2.7K observed coming from all directions in space. *(See also* ATOM; STELLAR EVOLUTION).

binary star two stars held together by their mutual gravity in orbit around each other. Each star usually follows an elliptical orbit and this is centred on the BARYCENTRE. About $\frac{2}{3}$ of the stars in our own MILKY WAY GALAXY are binary or multiple star systems. Several types are recognized (*see* VISUAL BINARY, ECLIPSING BINARY, SPECTROSCOPIC BINARY, POLARIZATION BINARY). If the orbits of binary star systems can be determined by any means, then much information about the individual stars, which cannot be inferred by other methods, can be obtained: masses, sizes, densities, velocities, separations and even the presence of other bodies too faint to be seen.

black body radiation ELECTROMAGNETIC RADIATION with a particular distribution characteristic of that from an ideal black body, i.e. one that perfectly absorbs and emits all WAVELENGTHS of the electromagnetic spectrum. Many astronomical objects approximate to black bodies, and a graph of their energy output against wavelength has the characteristic form shown in the diagram below.

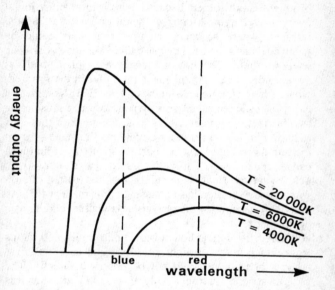

The middle curve is for a star at 6000K, i.e. like the Sun, and the peak of the EMISSION SPECTRUM is nearly in the middle of the visible region, thus the Sun has a yellowish appearance with a deficiency at both the blue and the red end of the visible spectrum. The higher curve is for a star with a surface temperature of about 20,000K. The curve is of identical form, but higher at every wavelength, and the peak is well into the ULTRAVIOLET. The star would appear blue because the curve is rising from a low level at the red end of the visible to a high level in the blue. The lowest curve is for a star with a surface temperature of 4000K. The star appears red, with little emission in the blue and the peak is in the INFRARED. The hotter star would appear brighter than the others because there is more emission at every wavelength. Much of the ultraviolet and of the infrared, where so much energy from stars could be received, cannot be used because there are no ATMOSPHERIC WINDOWS there. The EARTH radiates as a black body at about 300K. The peak of this curve is far in the infrared, where there are few windows. The Earth's radiation experiences absorption by its own atmosphere thus acting as a blanket to prevent energy loss. The peak of the sun's radiation is in an atmospheric window, thus energy from the Sun more easily reaches Earth than energy from Earth can escape to space. This is the GREENHOUSE EFFECT.

black dwarf the final stage in STELLAR EVOLUTION, often a WHITE DWARF star that has exhausted all its nuclear fuel. As it cools it becomes progressively less visible, ending as a black dwarf.

black hole a theoretical body of great mass and small radius from which not even light could escape; as a CELESTIAL BODY, a black hole could not be observed directly. The ESCAPE VELOCITY, V, from a body of mass M and radius R is given by $V = \sqrt{(2GM/R)}$ where G is the constant of universal GRAVITATION. The larger the mass M and the smaller the radius R, the greater becomes the velocity V needed for any particle to escape from the gravitational attraction of the body. At the limit when V becomes the velocity of light, C, not even light can escape. A black hole of mass M has a maximum radius R_s, given by $R_s = 2GM/C^2$, known as the SCHWARZCHILD RADIUS. The black hole is surrounded by an EVENT HORIZON beyond which it is invisible to an outside observer.

A STAR which has burned away its nuclear fuel has no radioactive energy to sustain it, so it collapses under its own gravity. A star three times bigger than the Sun could collapse to a black hole of less than 10km radius with an enormous mass. If this process should occur then there would be many black holes in all GALAXIES, their presence being revealed only by intense, very local gravitational effects. It is thought that many X-ray sources (Cygnus X-1 is an example) may consist of a BINARY STAR system where one member is a black hole and the other has evolved to a RED GIANT. The black hole robs its companion, sucking in its outer gas layers, the acceleration and collisions of this swirling gas generating X-rays. It is considered that the nuclei of galaxies may also contain large black holes.

Bodes law *see* **Titius-Bode law**.

Bok globules relatively small (10^3 to 10^5 astronomical units) dark nebulae in the MILKY WAY GALAXY, lying in regions where there is not much other gas. Some appear to be contracting under gravity, and it is thought that they may condense into stars in a time of the order of 10 years.

bolometer an instrument for the absorption and measurement of all radiation energy falling upon it, capable of covering the whole ELECTROMAGNETIC SPECTRUM.

Boltzmann equation an equation linking the absolute or Kelvin temperature, T, to the average kinetic energy of a particle.

Bonner Durchmusterung (the Bonn Survey) a star catalogue listing the position and magnitude of 324,188 northern stars. The culmination of 25 years work by the German astronomer Argelander, based at Bonn, the charts were issued in 1863 and reissued in 1950.

Boötes a northern sky CONSTELLATION. The brightest star, Alpha Boötes, is also known as Arcturas. The QUADRANTID meteor stream seems to have its RADIANT in the constellation.

boson a subatomic particle whose spin is an integral number.

Boss General Catalogue a star catalogue started by the American astronomer Lewis Boss in 1895, planned to give the positions and motions of stars in the northern hemisphere as seen from Albany and in the southern hemisphere from Argentina. The Preliminary General Catalogue was published in 1910, two years before Boss died. The work was completed by his son Benjamin in 1937, giving 33, 342 stars.

Brans-Dicke theory the theory that the constant of universal gravitation, G, occurring in Newton's Law of gravitation, $F=G(_1M_2/r^2)$, (where F is the force due to gravity between two masses M_1 and M_2 a distance r apart) is not constant. As a result of the EXPANDING UNIVERSE G would change by 2 parts in 10^{11} every year.

bremsstrahlung electromagnetic radiation emitted or absorbed when a free electron is decelerated or accelerated by the electric field of a nucleus without being captured by it. It is the principal method by which X-RAYS are produced. The word is German and means 'braking radiation'.

brightness the subjective visual sensation related to intensity of light. *See also* LUMINOSITY.

brightness temperature the temperature of a BLACK BODY which emits radiation of the observed intensity at a given wavelength. *See also* STEFAN-BOLTZMANN LAW; COLOUR TEMPERATURE.

brown star a name give to a possible CELESTIAL OBJECT

intermediate between a planet and a star. An accumulation of stellar material less than 0.08 that of the Sun would not develop internal pressures and temperatures at which nuclear fusion reactions could commence. A brown star is a star that has failed to ignite. The planet JUPITER is a possible example.

B star *see* **spectral classification**.

butterfly diagram a diagram showing the variation of solar latitude with time for the first appearance of SUNSPOTS through the 11 year sunspot cycle. It is so called from the appearance of the diagram, like butterfly wings.

C

calendar any system by which the beginning, length and subdivision of time into recognized periods is achieved. From ancient times the day was recognized as the pre-eminent natural division, the PHASES of the Moon gave rise to the month and the cycle of the seasons to the year. The basic difficulty in forming a consistent calendar is that these obvious natural divisions do not mesh together. It takes about 365¼ days for the Earth to make one orbit, a new Moon appears every 29½ days.

A variety of systems were adopted by the Egyptians, Romans and due to accumulated discrepancies Pope Gregory III again reformed the calendar to give the Gregorian Calendar; 10 days were omitted from October 1582 and only centennial years divisible by 400 were to be counted as leap years. As accuracy of observation improved, it became obvious that neither the spin of the EARTH nor its orbital period were in any way constant, and a new method of determining time was required. This was found in the atomic clock, and the second became the unit of time. Days and years are now defined in terms of IAT (International Atomic Time), whose basic unit is the second, and are now periodically adjusted to agree with this time scale.

Callisto a Galilean satellite of JUPITER, observed in 1610 with a diameter of 4800 km. It is probably a mixture of rock and ice, with a nearly circular orbit of 1.88 x 10⁶ km

radius. It has one massive impact basin, known as
Valhalla, of diameter about 600km.

Caloris basin the largest feature on Mercury, an impact
crater 1300 km in diameter.

Calypso a satellite of Saturn. The irregular body, of
dimensions 34 x 22 x 22 km is in a circular orbit of 294 x
10^3 km radius.

canals on Mars a network of fine lines at the limit of
visibility from Earth, which were thought to be evidence
of an irrigation system. First studied by Schiaparelli in
1877 and principally by Lowell at Flagstaff Observatory
in Arizona, they are now known to be in the main isolated
markings and not continuous features.

Cancer a zodiacal constellation, the Crab, between Leo and
Gemini at 8 hours 25 minutes RIGHT ASCENSION and 20°
north DECLINATION. It has no bright stars, none brighter than
4th MAGNITUDE. There is a large STAR CLUSTER, M44, known
as the Beehive or Praesepe, in the constellation.

Canes Venatici a CONSTELLATION of the northern sky. The
brightest star, Alpha Canum Veneticorum, is a binary of
the 3rd MAGNITUDE. It was named *Cor Caroli* ('the heart
of Charles') by Halley in honour of Charles II. The most
famous feature of the constellation is M51, the
Whirlpool GALAXY. There is also a GLOBULAR CLUSTER, M3
or NGC 5272, which may be seen with the aid of
binoculars.

Canis Major a CONSTELLATION of the southern sky, 'the
Greater Dog'. The brightest star, Alpha Canis Majoris, is
the brightest of all stars (apart from the Sun) and is a hot
DWARF STAR with a faint WHITE DWARF companion. It is
known as Sirius and also as the Dog Star and was used by
the ancient Egyptians as the basis of their calendar.

Canis Minor a northern sky CONSTELLATION, 'the Lesser

Dog'. The brightest star, Alpha Canis Minoris, also known as Procyon, is of 1st magnitude and is a visual BINARY STAR, one component being a DWARF STAR rather hotter than the SUN, with a WHITE DWARF companion.

Canopus (Alpha Carinae) a star of 1st magnitude and the brightest star in the CONSTELLATION CARINA. It is second only to Sirius (Canis Major) in brightness and is a young, POPULATION I, hot GIANT STAR.

Capella (Alpha Aurigae) a star of 1st magnitude and the brightest star in the constellation Auriga; it is the sixth brightest star in the sky. It is a BINARY STAR, with two GIANT STARS having a surface temperature close to that of the Sun, orbiting each other every 104 days.

Capricornus a zodiacal constellation lying between AQUARIUS and SAGITTARIUS at 21 hours RIGHT ASCENSION and 20° south DECLINATION. The brightest star, Alpha Capricorni, also known as Algedi or Giedi, is a BINARY STAR visible to the unaided eye. Both components are 4th MAGNITUDE.

carbonaceous chondrite a STONY METEORITE containing granules known as CHONDRULES. It is thought to have a relatively high carbon content.

carbon cycle (also known as the carbon-nitrogen cycle or Bethe cycle) is thought to be the principal nuclear fusion reaction responsible for the energy of many MAIN SEQUENCE STARS. It requires a temperature of about 1.8×10^7K, (above that in the core of the Sun where a PROTON-PROTON CHAIN reaction dominates) and involves the fusion of hydrogen to helium through a sequence of nuclear reactions involving carbon, nitrogen and oxygen. The complete cycle involves a loss of mass, the MASS DEFECT, which is converted to energy, also releasing GAMMA RAYS and NEUTRINOS (*see also* ATOM). The complete cycle is:

$$^{12}C + {}^{1}H \longrightarrow {}^{13}N + \gamma$$
$$^{13}N \longrightarrow {}^{13}C + \beta^{+} + \upsilon$$
$$^{13}C + {}^{1}H \longrightarrow {}^{14}N + \gamma$$
$$^{14}N + {}^{1}H \longrightarrow {}^{15}O + \gamma$$
$$^{15}O \longrightarrow {}^{15}N + \beta^{+} + \upsilon$$
$$^{15}N + {}^{1}H \longrightarrow {}^{12}C + \alpha$$

It therefore starts by fusing a PROTON, ^{1}H, with a carbon nucleus, ^{12}C, to give an ISOTOPE of nitrogen, ^{13}N, and releasing energy in the form of heat and a gamma ray. Three more PROTONS are successively added with release of heat energy, gamma rays, neutrinos and positrons, before the reconstitution of the nucleus of ^{12}C on which the cycle started along with the alpha particle, i.e. the helium nucleus. Thus hydrogen has been transmitted to helium, and the carbon, which acts as a sort of catalyst, returned to start another cycle.

carbon star *see* **Wolf-Rayet star**.

Carina a southern sky constellation, the brightest star of which, Alpha Carinae, is also known as CANOPUS.

Carme a small satellite of Jupiter. It is about 30km in diameter and is in an elliptical orbit of about 22,000 km radius, which is unusual in that it has a high inclination to Jupiter's equator and the satellite is in RETROGRADE motion.

cartwheel galaxy a galaxy, A0035, of unusual shape. Seen from EARTH there is a central hub of older, mainly red, stars. Surrounding this is a vast ring of spectacular brilliant blue and white stars. Spiral 'spikes' appear to connect the hub to the outer rim. The whole galaxy is of comparable size to our own MILKY WAY system. The highly unusual form of this galaxy is thought to have arisen some hundreds of millions of years ago from a 'collision' between two existing galaxies creating an enormous number of big new STARS in the ring. Many of these new stars were too massive and therefore too hot to have long lives, and it is found that the number of SUPERNOVAE in the Cartwheel Galaxy is about a hundred times greater than that expected from a galaxy of this size. The other galaxy involved has not been positively identified, as there are two possible candidates in the CLUSTER.

Cassegrain telescope a form of REFLECTING TELESCOPE.

Cassini's division a dark gap between the two principal bands of Saturn's rings.

Cassiopeia a northern sky CONSTELLATION, 1 hour RIGHT ASCENSION, 60° north DECLINATION. The five brightest stars appear as an irregular W-shape, and the centre one, Gamma Cassiopeia, is a SHELL STAR, and variable star of inconsistent period. Cassiopeia A is a strong radio source.

Cassiopeia A *see* **Cassiopeia**.

Castor (Alpha Geminorum) the brightest star in the constellation Gemini. It is a MULTIPLE STAR with six components: two hot DWARF STARS are in a 500-year orbit round each other and each in turn is a SPECTROSCOPIC BINARY; a third component, YY Gemimorum, is an ECLIPSING BINARY system with both components FLARE STARS.

cataclysmic variable a star which suddenly changes its brightness by several magnitudes. Many are close BINARY STARS where one fills its ROCHE LOBE and loses material by the gravitational attraction of its companion. The increase in brightness is due to nuclear fusion reactions taking place on the surface of the receiving star.

catalogue a collection of data about celestial objects, stars, nebulae, galaxies, etc. For stars, the earliest catalogues were, perhaps, the ancient collection of recognized CONSTELLATIONS, although these were no more than fanciful groupings of usually quite unconnected relatively bright stars forming chance patterns. Many of the constellations have been retained, however, as a simple method of identifying the particular region of the celestial sphere assigned to them and their usefulness extended by signifying the brightest stars by BAYER LETTERS. Modern star catalogues usually list the star's position on the celestial sphere for a particular EPOCH in terms of the two arcs, RIGHT ASCENSION and DECLINATION, as well as some of the following: MAGNITUDE, PARALLAX, PROPER MOTION, RADIAL VELOCITY, COLOUR INDEX and SPECTRAL CLASS, as well as indicating such special features as variability and companions if part of a BINARY or MULTIPLE STAR system.

celestial body any object in the sky which can be studied, usually identified by its position on the CELESTIAL SPHERE.

celestial co-ordinates *see* **celestial sphere**.

celestial equator *see* **celestial sphere.**

celestial mechanics the study of the motion, etc, of celestial bodies, usually under gravitation. *See also* ASTRONOMY.

celestial object *see* **celestial body**.

celestial poles *see* **celestial sphere**.

celestial sphere for many purposes it is useful to think of all celestial bodies, regardless of distance from Earth, as if in position on the inside of a sphere of undetermined radius and having the observer on the Earth at the centre. This sphere is the celestial sphere. As the Earth rotates about its axis, it give the observer the impression that the celestial sphere is rotating in the opposite direction round him, spinning on an axis through the north and south celestial poles. This axis passes through the Earth's poles and the centre of the Earth and thus coincides with the Earth's axis. Further, the Earth's equator, if imagined extended out to reach the celestial sphere, would lie along the celestial equator. To locate the position of any object on the celestial sphere requires two celestial co-ordinates corresponding to longitude and latitude on Earth's surface. Different systems are in use—ALTAZIMUTH, EQUATORIAL and ecliptic. The following refers to the equatorial system. On Earth the zero of longitude is taken to be the Greenwich meridian, the imaginary arc laid out over the Earth's surface, running from pole to pole and passing through Greenwich. On the celestial sphere the corresponding meridian is an arc laid out over the inside surface of the celestial sphere and passing through a particular point on the celestial equator. The particular point chosen is known as the VERNAL EQUINOX or First point of Aries. A measurement made in degrees from this point on the zero meridian eastwards along the celestial equator is called the RIGHT ASCENSION. On Earth the other co-ordinate is the latitude, measured along another meridian as degrees north or south of the equator. The equivalent measurement on the celestial sphere is called the DECLINATION, measured again in degrees along another meridian north or south of the celestial equator. The diagram opposite the shows these angular measures. The right ascension may be expressed as a time, in hours, minutes and seconds rather than in degrees on the basis that the celestial sphere makes one revolution, i.e. turns 360º in one day, or 15° in 1 hour. So, for instance, a right ascension of 36° could be expressed as $1/10$ of a day, i.e. 2.4 hours or a right ascension of 2 hr 24 minutes.

Observers sometimes prefer to measure the right ascension from their own locality rather than from the zero meridian. In this case the meridian on the celestial sphere which passes vertically overhead at the observatory, the local meridian, is determined and its right ascension from the zero meridian found. Objects located on the celestial sphere by this observatory can then have their measured right ascensions corrected by the addition of the right ascension of their local meridian, called the LOCAL HOUR ANGLE.

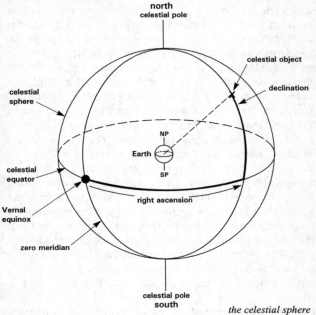

the celestial sphere

Centaurus a southern sky constellation. The brightest stars, Alpha Centauri, (or Rigil Kentaurus), and BETA CENTAURI (Hadar or Agena) are both of 1st magnitude and act as POINTERS to the Southern Cross or CRUX. Omega Centauri, which appears as a 4th MAGNITUDE diffusive star to the unaided eye, is in fact the largest and brightest GLOBULAR CLUSTER.

Centaurus A an ELLIPTICAL GALAXY in the constellation CENTAURUS. It is a strong RADIO GALAXY as well as having infrared, visible and gamma ray emissions.

centimetric radio radio transmission and reception at wavelengths of a few centimetres. The field is important is studying the vast clouds of un-ionized HYDROGEN gas in the UNIVERSE, which would otherwise be invisible.

centre of mass for a body of irregular shape, or for a system of separate bodies, it is possible to locate a point, not necessarily in a body, where the whole mass of the body or bodies appears to act. For instance, in a BINARY STAR system the two components will be in orbit round each other. It can lead to much simplification to think of each compartment in orbit around the one point, the centre of mass or BARYCENTRE. The term 'centre of gravity' is also used.

centripetal force a moving body with no forces of any kind acting on it will move in a straight line at constant VELOCITY. A body moving in a circle (or ellipse) requires a force directed to the centre of the circle (or one FOCUS of the ellipse) to make the body follow the curved circular path. This directed force is called the centripetal force. For a mass M moving in a circular orbit of radius R at a constant speed V, the centripetal force F is given by $F = MV^2/R$.

Cepheid variable one of a class of regular VARIABLE STARS, the prototype of which is Delta Cephei. Typically, Cepheids are brighter stars which can be seen over great distances, the brightness changing by about one MAGNITUDE and the periods ranging from 1 to 50 days. Spectroscopic studies of Cepheids using the DOPPLER EFFECT have shown that the whole star is pulsing, the bigger the star, the longer the period and the brighter it appears. About twenty local galaxies have had their distances measured using Cepheid variables.

Cepheus a north sky constellation close to the pole. Delta Cephei, the prototype for CEPHEID VARIABLES, is also a BINARY STAR with the 4th magnitude yellow variable star having a 6th magnitude blue/white companion. Mu Cephei, also known as the Garnet Star, is a red supergiant.

Cerenkov radiation electromagnetic radiation emitted when highly energetic particles travelling close to the velocity of light enter a medium in which they are moving faster than the velocity of light in that medium.

Ceres an ASTEROID that, at over 1000 km diameter, was the first to be found in the asteroid belt in response to the suggestion in the TITIUS-BODE law that there might be a planet in the orbit between Mars and Jupiter.

Cetus an equatorial constellation. The star Mira Ceti, also known as Omicron Ceti, is a long period variable and is the prototype for a class of variable star.

chain reaction a reaction, whether chemical or nuclear, in which the reaction proceeds in stages, the products of one stage forming the reactants for the next. Chain reactions form the basis of many nuclear fission and fusion reactions. *See also* CARBON CYCLE.

Chandler wobble a periodic movement of the Earth's rotation axis which causes LATITUDE to vary with a period of about 14 months. It is a PRECESSION of the Earth's axis of rotation about its axis of symmetry caused by asymmetry of the Earth.

Chandrasekkar limit the maximum mass of a white dwarf star, about 1.44 times the Sun's mass. Above this limit the GRAVITATIONAL FORCES crush the core material to form a NEUTRON STAR or BLACK HOLE.

chaos a state of confusion and unpredictability. Chaos, in a technical sense, is used to describe a complex interrelated, moving or dynamic system where known physical laws govern the behaviour but where the complexity is such that a slight alteration in some part of the system has consequences which seem quite unpredictable. An example is the EARTH's weather systems. The Earth's atmosphere is subject to well-known physical laws, but it is so sensitive to change that even small causes can have large and often unpredictable consequences. The understanding of chaos, chaos theory is of fundamental importance in astronomy as in all science.

charge-coupled device (CCD) a light-sensitive semiconductor chip which is divided into a regular array of small areas called pixels. It is exposed, as an alternative to a photographic film, at the focus of a telescope where the image of an astronomical object is formed. The charge liberated by the light falling on the device is more linearly related to the INTENSITY of the light than is a photographic film, and the SENSITIVITY is high. Further, by operating at low temperature, a very clean image is obtained. At the end of the exposure, the charge accumulated at each pixel is read out in sequence and stored until convenient for analysis. Because of the very linear response to light intensity a CCD is often used as the sensitive element in PHOTOMETRY.

Charon the only satellite of Pluto so far discovered (1978). It has a diameter of 1,200 km, about half that of Pluto, and its orbital period, uniquely in the Solar System, is the same as Pluto's SPIN-PERIOD.

Chiron an ASTEROID discovered in 1977. It is in an eccentric orbit that takes it out well beyond Saturn, and it may have a faint COMA, suggesting that in some respects it resembles a COMET. The orbit is unstable and much affected by the gravitational pull of the major planets.

chondrite a METEORITE, stony, and containing granules known as CHONDRULES. Chondrites were probably created at the same time as the Solar System, some 4.6 thousand million years ago, and may be representative of the original material formed. The class comprises carbonaceous chondrites, with a considerable carbon content, enstatites containing $MgSiO_3$, and most common of all, ordinary chondrites. Stony meteorites without chondrites are known as ACHONDRITES.

chondrule small nodule-like grains formed from solidified drops of once molten rock. *See also* CHONDRITES.

chromatic aberration an image imperfection occurring in optical instruments using lenses. The REFRACTIVE INDEX of the material of a lens varies with WAVELENGTH, hence a lens has a different focal length for each wavelength, or colour, of light. The effect on an image formed from WHITE LIGHT is to give coloured edges to details of the image.

chromosphere a layer in a star's atmosphere (including the Sun). It is a layer, above the REVERSING LAYER and PHOTOSPHERE and below the CORONA, which can be seen as a thin red circle surrounding the outline of the Moon during a total Solar eclipse. The chromosphere is thousands of kilometres thick and consists chiefly of hydrogen, helium and calcium; it is the origin of FLARES and PROMINENCES, and SPICULES are present.

circumpolar stars stars which, in any given latitude, never 'set' by dipping below the horizon; they seem to revolve around the poles of the CELESTIAL SPHERE. An observer situated at the north pole of the Earth would see the stars in the northern hemisphere night sky circling round the celestial pole, those near the horizon describing circles of large radius parallel to the horizon with smaller concentric circles traced out by stars at a higher angle of DECLINATION. Any star situated at the celestial pole would appear to remain fixed. Conversely, an observer situated on the equator of the Earth facing east would see the night sky stars on the CELESTIAL EQUATOR rise from his horizon, describe a great circular arc about his head and set behind him on the western horizon. Stars with higher angles of declination to the north or south would describe smaller radii semi-circles. Theoretically, only stars situated at the poles of the celestial sphere would appear stationary and thus never dip below his horizon. A camera laid on its back on a horizontal surface and left undisturbed with the lens pointing vertically upwards and the shutter open for some time on a clear night will show the arcs of light traced out by stars apparently circling round the celestial pole.

civil year the calendar year as used in ordinary life, consisting of 365 days in ordinary years and 366 in leap years. It is kept in step with the astronomical year by relatively frequent slight adjustments.

closed universe *see* **universe**.

cluster of galaxies galaxies are not scattered uniformly throughout the universe but tend to be in groups or clusters with relatively larger distances between the clusters. The LOCAL GROUP, includes our own MILKY WAY GALAXY, the two MAGELLANIC CLOUDS and the ANDROMEDA GALAXY, has at least seventeen members and represents three different types of galaxy: 5 spirals, 10 elliptical and 2 irregular. Other, more distant clusters may have more members, e.g. the Coma Cluster has 1000 members and the Virgo Cluster has 2500. There is some evidence for SUPER CLUSTERS or clusters of clusters existing.

cluster of stars *see* **star cluster**.

coelostat a flat mirror on a mechanically driven mounting which is so arranged as to direct the light from any selected area of sky constantly onto some observing instrument. It is used to counteract, for instance, the APPARENT MOTION of the heavens produced by the SPIN of the EARTH, especially where it is inconvenient to move the observing instrument.

collimator an apparatus for forming light into a parallel beam. It is particularly used in SPECTROMETRY.

colour index a simplified method of classifying stars by using coloured light filters to find the most significant features of their spectra. A star is assigned to a given class by examining the spectrum of its emitted light and then by comparison determining its spectral class; or, determining its SPECTRAL INDEX; or, finding its place in the spectral sequence: all these terms are used, to some extent interchangeably. Obtaining and examining spectra from many stars is a formidable task. A simpler method is to find the principal features of a star's spectrum by recording its APPARENT MAGNITUDE in different parts of the visible or near-visible spectrum. In a widely used system three determinations of apparent magnitude are made: U, B and V. U is through a filter passing only ultraviolet and violet; B is through a filter passing only blue; V is through a filter passing only the peak of the visible spectrum, in the green/yellow. The colour indices are then (U-B) and (B-V) which may be negative. Hence it is easy to see the chief characteristic of any given star spectrum. A cool RED STAR will have almost no U-magnitude but considerable V-magnitude. Conversely, a hot blue star will have a larger U-magnitude than V-magnitude, etc. Basically it is a simple wholesale method of determining the BLACK BODY curve of a star, from which its temperature and much else can be found. The technique lends itself to photography, as all that is required is to take three successive photographs of the same region of the CELESTIAL SPHERE through the three filters. It can be also be used with old photographic plates taken last century and comparing them with later photographs of the same sky region, for old photographic emulsions were sensitive only to ultraviolet and violet. Later ones had more green and yellow sensitivity, so approximate colour indices could be found.

colour temperature the temperature of a, usually inaccessible, incandescent body determined by comparing its EMISSION SPECTRUM with that of a BLACK BODY whose temperature can be adjusted until the two match. *See also* BRIGHTNESS TEMPERATURE.

coma (1) in optics, a form of ABERRATION in optical instruments in which a point image is distorted into a pear-shaped patch when it is not on the axis of the instrument. (2) in astronomy, a diffuse, almost spherical, cloud of gas and dust surrounding the head, or nucleus, of a COMET when it is near the Sun; a temporary atmosphere.

coma cluster *see* **cluster of galaxies**.

comet any of a class of small CELESTIAL OBJECTS which appear, often periodically, in very elliptical orbits round the Sun, having a HEAD surrounded by a COMA and a more or less long and often spectacular TAIL. Comets may come from a collection of icy fragments formed at the origin of the Solar System, some 4.6 thousand million years ago. It is not certain how comets come into orbits passing close to the Sun, but it is only the Sun's energy that reveals them and renders them the spectacular objects they can be. Far from the Sun, the nucleus is just a mass of loose-packed ice, dust grains and gas, perhaps of 1 km diameter. Whipple has likened it to a dirty snowball. The dust grains may be dark, containing carbon or carbon compounds. As the nucleus journeys towards the Sun, the solar energy causes some of the material to evaporate and spurt out, forming the coma round the nucleus. As more material is ejected into the coma, some is swept back by the SOLAR WIND to form the tail, which streams away from the Sun. All parts of the comet may scatter and reflect light from the Sun, and a spectacular display may result. Passing through PERIHELION, the comet starts its long journey away from the Sun, gradually losing the coma and tail as the material is dissipated into space, and losing brightness as the distance from the Sun increases. Many comets are periodic visitors, with longer or shorter intervals between returns. Encke's comet has one of the shortest periods, just over 3 years, and the better-known Halley's comet returns in just over 76 years. Some comets come quite close to the Sun, Halley's to within 0.6 astronomical unit, and thus it is possible for the Earth to pass through the orbit. The debris left by the passage of the comet forms a METEOR STREAM as the Earth sweeps through it.

comparator any device for comparing one item with another, or with a standard. One form which has been used in astronomy is the 'blink microscope'. This is essentially a double microscope enabling two photographs of the same region of the CELESTIAL SPHERE to be examined at the same time, one by one eye, the other by the other eye. A rotating shutter cuts off the image of each photograph alternately, and if the two photographs are identical and in register the alternately presented images are fused to give one unchanging view. If, however, there has been a small change of position of a star on one photograph as compared to the other, then the alternately presented images do not fuse, and the movement will cause the displaced star-image to appear to stand out from the background; thus small star movements can be detected in a mass of unchanging star positions.

Compton scattering the effect of an interaction of X-rays with electrons. The incident X-ray PHOTON has a particular energy and thus wavelength. If it interacts with an electron on its passage through matter, some of the X-ray energy is transferred to the electron. The loss of energy by the X-ray causes it to have a longer wavelength.

conic section a curve obtained by the intersection of a right circular cone by a plane. A hollow circular cone is standing upright on its flat base. A plane is cut across the cone parallel to the base. The cut across the surface of the cone is in the form of a circle. If the plane is cut across the cone not quite parallel to the base but not so slanted as to cut across the base, the result is an ellipse, and the less parallel to the base is the cut the more eccentric, i.e. less like a circle, is the ellipse. If the cut is at an angle such that the plane of the cut is parallel to an 'edge' of the cone, the result is a parabola, a curve that never closes. Finally a steeper cut yet produces a hyperbola.

conjunction an approximate lining up of three CELESTIAL BODIES. As an example, consider the Sun and Earth as being two of the bodies and one of the planets as the third. Two cases are distinct, one where the planet is an INFERIOR PLANET, i.e. in an orbit smaller than that of the Earth, e.g. Venus; the other for a SUPERIOR PLANET, e.g. Mars. On occasion, Earth, Venus and the Sun will all be in a straight line. If Venus is between Earth and Sun, it is called an INFERIOR CONJUNCTION, and if Venus is on the other side of the Sun from the Earth, it is a SUPERIOR CONJUNCTION.

Again, on occasion, Mars, Earth and Sun are all in a straight line. If Mars is on the opposite side of the Sun from the Earth, it is said to be in *conjunction*, whereas if Earth lies between Mars and the Sun, Mars is said to be in *opposition*. It is rare for planets ever to be properly aligned as their orbits do not lie exactly in the same plane. On the rare occasions when one of the inferior planets, Mercury or Venus, does come between the Earth and the Sun, it makes a TRANSIT across the Sun's disk.

constellation one of 88 recognized groupings of usually unconnected relatively prominent stars, which by chance form a noticeable, though often fanciful, pattern in a region of the CELESTIAL SPHERE. Constellations are of ancient origin—of 48 listed in the ALMAGEST many had been absorbed into Greek culture from older civilizations. Largely, the names and star-groupings have survived although some changes have been made. The current list of 88 was officially adopted by the International Astronomical Union in 1922, and in 1930 the IAU approved for each constellation agreed boundaries. drawn on the celestial sphere along lines of RIGHT ASCENSION and DECLINATION. The constellations have been retained in modern positional astronomy as they are a simple and relatively clear way of indicating an area of interest on the celestial sphere. For instance, the object correctly identified in CATALOGUES as M31 or NGC 24 is more usually referred to simply as the Great ANDROMEDA GALAXY, as it lies within the boundaries of the constellation ANDROMEDA.

The twelve constellations of the ZODIAC are those through which the Sun appears to move on its annual journey at the rate of approximately one every month. The others divide the celestial sphere into irregularly shaped areas.

Astronomical references may be made across the constellation boundaries. Examples are the POINTER STARS.

continuous spectrum the complete and unbroken range of electromagnetic waves form a continuous spectrum. The conventional subdivision into regions, e.g. gamma rays, visible light, radio waves, is for convenience only and in recognition that generating or detecting in particular regions is best done by methods particular to that region. For many practical purposes shorter ranges may be regarded as forming a continuous spectrum within certain limits, for instance light from an incandescent filament bulb is called white light, implying that all wavelengths in the visible spectrum are present at not too dissimilar intensities, but the emission of gamma rays and long radio waves is negligible. The emission spectrum of the filament is similar to that of a black body, for which the curve of intensity against wavelength has a completely specific shape depending only on the temperature, this is used to measure filament temperature by comparison with a BLACK BODY.

The visible light from a star often may be regarded as a continuous spectrum. As the star radiates rather like a black body, measuring the intensity of light as a function of wavelength for the star's spectrum, the SPECTRAL DISTRIBUTOR, allows the temperature of the radiating surface to be found. However, close examination of the spectrum of the SUN reveals that it is crossed by numerous dark FRAUNHOFER LINES, caused by ABSORPTION of light by ATOMS in cooler layers overlying the radiating surface. The continuous emission spectrum has thus a discontinuous ABSORPTION SPECTRUM superimposed, and this absorption has to be allowed for in determining the temperature of the emitting surface. It also allows for identification of the atoms present. Similarly, stellar spectra can show bright emission lines from excited atoms. The background continuous spectrum has thus a superimposed discontinuous emission spectrum. This emission spectrum also reveals much about the ELEMENTS present and their state of IONIZATION; but it, too, may also require to be allowed for in measuring the star's temperature. Thus although the visible light from a star may for some purposes and with advantage be regarded as a sufficient approximation to a continuous spectrum, it must always be remembered that more detailed examination may reveal other influences at work for which allowance may be made and from which more information may be available.

convection zone a region where heat energy is principally carried by convection currents, i.e. by movement of a fluid from regions at a higher temperature to regions at a lower one. The SUN has a convection zone some 400,000km thick in which the ENERGY produced in the FUSION REACTIONS of the CORE is conveyed to the visible region, the PHOTOSPHERE. The top of the convection currents rising through the zone give rise to visible features called granulation, seen on the PHOTOSPHERE.

co-ordinate system a system of numbers, essentially representing lengths, indicating the position of a required point relative to the origin or starting point. In ASTRONOMY, the two co-ordinates needed to locate a CELESTIAL OBJECT on the CELESTIAL SPHERE are often the RIGHT ASCENSION and the DECLINATION. *See also* CELESTIAL SPHERE.

Copernican system a picture of the SOLAR SYSTEM introduced in 1543 by Copernicus to replace the Ptolemaic system, which had been in use for over 14 centuries. In the Ptolemaic system, the EARTH was taken to be the centre of the Universe and all CELESTIAL BODIES, including the SUN, revolved in circular ORBITS round it; it was a geocentric picture. As more accurate observations were made it became necessary to consider the PLANETS not just in orbit around the Earth, but to have epicyclical motion as well, i.e. small circular orbits round their main geocentric orbit. Further improved accuracy of observation required even more modifications to the Ptolemaic geocentric picture, and Copernicus realized that a much simpler picture arose if the Sun became the centre of the system and the Earth just another planet in an orbit around it. It was a Sun-centred, or heliocentric, model and fitted the observed motions without need for epicycles. Only the Moon was left to orbit.

Cor Caroli *see* **Canes Venatici**.

Cordelia a small, 50km-diameter satellite of Uranus. It is in a circular orbit of radius about 50×10^3 km.

core the central part of anything. In astronomy it usually refers to the innermost, usually spherical, heart of any CELESTIAL OBJECT. For instance, the planet Jupiter is thought to have a core of rock surrounded by a liquid envelope. The core of the Sun, or any MAIN SEQUENCE STAR, is the central region where the temperature and pressure are high enough for the NUCLEAR FUSION reactions to take place.

Coriolis force an imaginary force that appears to operate on a body moving over a rotating one, e.g. a body moving in a straight line in space would appear, to an observer carried round on the rotating Earth, to have a curved path and thus to be subjected to a force. Although it is only an apparent force, it can have real enough effects as it is the origin of the forces that drive atmospheric systems, causing wind to flow round a depression instead of into the low pressure.

corona the outermost region of the Sun's atmosphere, stretching from the top of the CHROMOSPHERE out into space. It is not usually visible but can be seen during a total ECLIPSE of the Sun as a diffuse halo of light with a structure of radial lines surrounding the dark disk of the Moon. It is a PLASMA and the structure is caused by interaction of the charged particles with the Sun's magnetic fields. FLARES and PROMINENCES also occur in this region, and material ejected from the corona forms the SOLAR WIND. An instrument known as a *coronagraph* enables an artificial eclipse to be arranged within the instrument, permitting study of the form and structure of the corona to be made at any time.

Corvus a southern sky CONSTELLATION.

cosmic dust *see* **dust**.

cosmic rays highly penetrating radiation. Two categories are recognized: primary rays are those arriving from space and secondary rays are produced by interaction of the primary rays with Earth's atmosphere. Primary rays are very fast-moving NUCLEI of atoms containing mainly protons and no electrons. The majority come from within our own MILKY WAY GALAXY, perhaps from SUPERNOVAE; a few of the most energetic may come from beyond our Galaxy. Secondary rays are produced as a cascade of particles when a primary particle interacts with atoms in the upper atmosphere. By the time these cascades, or showers, reach Earth's surface they consist mainly of muons, electrons and photons. The rate of arrival seems to be very constant, only slightly affected by solar activity.

Cosmic rays produce the radioactive isotope ^{14}C, which is taken up by living organisms during life and undergoes radioactive decay. This has given rise to the technique of radioaction dating.

cosmogony a study of the origins and development of the universe or of a particular system in the universe, e.g. planetary systems.

cosmology the study of the origin, evolution and structure of the universe as a whole. It includes the mathematical treatment of theories intended to explain the origin of the universe, its current observed state and its future fate. The BIG BANG THEORY is currently favoured, the rival STEADY STATE THEORY not being in agreement with current observations.

CP Catalogue the *True Visual Magnitude Photographic Star Atlas* (1850.0) by Christos Papadopoulos.

Crab Nebula (M1 and NGC1952) a NEBULA in the constellation TAURUS. It appears to be the remnant of a SUPERNOVA explosion of AD 1054, observed to be 'as bright as Venus' by Chinese astronomers. It is a roughly oval patch filled with bright gaseous filaments surrounding a central blue star. Photographs taken over many years show the whole structure to be expanding in all directions. Working backwards from the present size and rate of expansion agrees with an explosion in 1054. The light is strongly polarized and the nebula is also a strong RADIO SOURCE (Taurus A) and X-ray source (Taurus X1), thus covering the complete electromagnetic spectrum. The source of these emissions is SYNCHROTRON RADIATION generated by the spinning NEUTRON STAR. It is also a PULSAR, the Crab pulsar.

Crab Pulsar *see* **Crab Nebula**.

crater a bowl-shaped cavity formed by either volcanic activity or impact. Most satellites and planets exhibit cratering, especially the Moon, Mercury and Mars, and these are thought to be due to collision with smaller bodies soon after the formation of the Solar System. Generally the craters are approximately circular, vary greatly in size, have a raised rim and occasionally a central peak, and often overlie each other. Volcanic craters are also known and have been identified on Venus, Mars and the Moon, although all seem to be extinct; but on Io, a satellite of Jupiter, the whole surface is dominated by volcanic activity. Similar impact craters may have existed on Earth, but subsequent activity, e.g. weathering and mountain forming, has removed all traces.

Crater a southern sky CONSTELLATION, the brightest STARS are 4th magnitude.

crepe ring one of the rings of Saturn, discovered by Dawes in 1850.

Cressida a small, 60km-diameter satellite of Uranus, in a circular orbit of 62×10^3 km radius.

crust the outer skin of a relatively newly formed planet or satellite. During formation of a substantial body by ACCRETION of smaller masses, much energy is liberated and most members of the Solar System were in a molten state. Subsequently the outer surface cooled down by radiating heat to space and solidified, forming a crust but leaving the interior molten. Impact on the crust by smaller bodies produced craters, and the molten rock from deeper in the body could ooze out as lava to flood the impact crater. If the composition of the original crust and the later lava flow were different, then the ALBEDO of the two areas would differ, making the craters more visible.

Crux a southern sky constellation. It is the smallest of all constellations. The brightest star, Alpha Crucis, is also known as ACRUX. Crux lies in a rich star field of the MILKY WAY GALAXY and has the Jewel Box cluster and some of the Coalsack nebula within its boundaries.

C-type asteroids *see* **asteroid**.

culmination the highest or lowest altitude, above or below the horizon, attained by a CELESTIAL OBJECT as it crosses the observer's MERIDIAN.

Cygnus a northern sky constellation. The brightest star, Alpha Cygni (also known as Deneb), is a 1st magnitude hot SUPERGIANT star. The second brightest, Beta Cygni (also known as Albireo), is a BINARY STAR which can be separated by a small telescope. One component is of 3rd magnitude and is orange, the other is of 5th magnitude and green.

Cygnus A in constellation Cygnus, the first RADIO GALAXY to be found and one of the brightest radio sources in the sky. It has a remarkably high radio output, which appears to come from two sources, but the mechanism is so far not understood.

Cygnus Loop also known as the Veil Nebula. Like the CRAB NEBULA this is the remnants of the outer layers of a STAR that exploded as a SUPERNOVA. The emission covers a wide range of the electromagnetic spectrum and is thought to be due to SYNCHROTRON RADIATION.

Cygnus X1 a BINARY STAR system identified by its X-ray emission. The intensity changes rapidly, suggesting a small source. It is possibly a SUPERGIANT and a BLACK HOLE in orbit round each other.

D

dark matter material which may exist in the universe but be 'invisible' in the sense that not only does it not shine with its own light nor yet reflect light, but further it reacts so rarely or weakly with the visible matter that it is difficult to detect in any way. Its main influence would be by gravitational attraction.

dark nebula *see* **absorption-nebula**.

Dawes limit an expression for the resolution obtained by a telescope used visually. Established by W.R. Dawes after whom a lunar crater is named.

day the time for one revolution of the earth about its axis. If this is taken as the time interval between two successive moons, i.e., the exact moment when the Sun is highest in the sky and thus nearest to overhead, then the day is not constant as the Earth travels in its elliptical orbit round the Sun at different speeds throughout the year. This led to the concept of the MEAN SOLAR DAY in which the seasonal variations are all averaged and an imaginary body, the mean sun, imagined to have an absolutely constant motion, is used to calculate the time of noon. For many astronomical purposes, however, it is more convenient to take the day as the time for one (apparent) rotation of the CELESTIAL SPHERE about the Earth, as this eliminates the need for correction due to the Earth's orbital movement. This day is referred to as the sidereal day and is measured as the time between successive passages across the observer's MERIDIAN of a specific point on the celestial sphere known as the VERNAL EQUINOX or First Point in Aries.

decay the decrease in amplitude or intensity with time. In RADIOACTIVITY the concept is used in determining the rate at which the number of radioactive ATOMS in a sample changes. Suppose at any instant there are N_o radioactive atoms present and at a time t this has dropped to a number N, then $N = N_o e^{-t}$ where is the decay constant. This is an example of exponential decay. It is possible to define a half-life for the radioactive material, i.e. the time, $t^{1/2}$, at which $N = \frac{1}{2}N_o$ i.e., $\frac{1}{2} No = No e^{-2t}$ $\frac{1}{2} \Rightarrow t_{1/2} = \frac{0.693}{\lambda}$.

Radio carbon dating makes use of the known decay constant or half-life of the isotope ^{14}C.

deceleration parameter a parameter, or number, describing the rate at which the expansion of the universe is slowing down because of the gravitational attractions within it.

declination *see* **celestial sphere.**

declination axis an axle permitting an instrument, e.g., a telescope, to be moved up and down to different angles of declination (see *also* ANGULAR MEASURE, CELESTIAL SPHERE).

declination circle a circle graduated in degrees and subdivisions allowing an instrument, e.g., a telescope suitably mounted, to be set to any required angle of declination (*see also* ANGULAR MEASURE, CELESTIAL SPHERE).

decoupling era an early period in the Big Bang theory when matter and radiation became distinct.

Deep Space Network a spacecraft communications network established by the American NASA organisation. It receives commands and telemetry from all kinds of spacecraft missions sent out into deep space.

degenerate star the inner core of a star is subject to enormous pressure from the weight of overlying layers.

So long as the material of the CORE is producing energy by NUCLEAR FUSION, the energy making its way out of the exterior exerts a counter pressure which prevents further gravitational collapse. Once the nuclear fuel is exhausted, however, the star starts to collapse under its own gravity. This raises the core temperature, as it is an ADIABATIC process, and also the density which can become of the order of 10^6 times that of water. Under these conditions the matter of the core is so compacted and crushed that it ceases to behave in the ordinary way; this form is called degenerate matter. A star with degenerate matter as its core is referred to as a degenerate star. WHITE DWARFS and NEUTRON STARS contain degenerate matter.

degree an ANGULAR MEASURE. A circle is subdivided into 360 equal sectors, each of one degree; further subdivisions are into 60 MINUTES each containing 60 SECONDS.

Deimos the outermost of two satellites of Mars, first located in 1877. It is small, with a diameter of about 12km, but very irregularly shaped. The surface is very irregular with considerable cratering, one crater being about 2.5km in diameter. It is of low density and the material may be similar to the CARBONACEOUS CHONDRITE METEORITES. The orbit is nearly circular and 23,460km from the planet's surface. Deimos keeps one face permanently turned to Mars.

Dembowska a small ASTEROID. Its orbit is close to the plane of the ECLIPTIC; an example of an S-type asteroid.

Deneb (Alpha Cygni) the brightest star in the constellation Cygnus.

density the mass of object expressed as ratio of the volume of object. The density of water is about 1,000 kgm^{-3}. It is often possible to find the volume of a member of the solar system by direct measurement; the mass can often be found from gravitational effects and thus a crude "average" density found. This can then be used to indicate the likely materials from which it is made, for instance, if a planet has a low density it is unlikely to have a metallic core. The density of the Sun is about 1,400kgm⁻³. Similarly, much information can be obtained about the components of a BINARY STAR system which in turn can be used to see if there is any unusual density associated with either component.

density wave often called shock wave. A sharp change in pressure, and thus density, in a narrow region in a gas caused by an explosion or other disturbance.

Desdemona small satellite of URANUS. It is 60km diameter in a circular orbit of 63,000km radius.

Despina a satellite of NEPTUNE of 180km diameter in an orbit of 53,000km radius.

deuterium an ISOTOPE of hydrogen having one NEUTRON as well as one PROTON in its NUCLEUS. It is important in several NUCLEAR REACTIONS relevant to ASTRONOMY, especially in the PROTON-PROTON CHAIN reaction which fuels our SUN. Although it is not a commonly occurring isotope, 0.015% of ordinary hydrogen, it has been used in the form of deuterium oxide, heavy water, in nuclear fission experiments.

diamond-ring effect an optical effect seen in the last stages of a total ECLIPSE of the Sun. When the Sun is just emerging from behind the shield of the Moon, the outer layers of the Sun's atmosphere appear first at one edge; then, as the two bodies continue to separate, the bright CHROMOSPHERE appears to form a ring spreading round the dark disk of the Moon. Finally the brilliant PHOTOSPHERE just emerges, giving the effect of a splendid diamond on the ring.

differential rotation a rotating solid body spins on its axis with every part of it making one revolution in the same period. This is not necessarily so in a fluid, liquid or gas. For instance, the Earth very largely spins as a solid, but the oceans and in particular the atmosphere do not and thus ocean and air currents are set up. JUPITER shows considerable differential rotation in its atmosphere, with parallel bands moving with respect to each other. This is a consequence of the fact that fluids cannot support shearing forces.

diffraction an effect experienced by all types of WAVE MOTION whereby the advancing wave appears to bend round any obstacle into the shadow region behind. The amount of diffraction depends upon the wavelength when the size of the obstacle is similar to the wavelength of the radiation the whole shadow region receives some radiation.

This is the reason for the blue sky. Molecules of the upper atmosphere form temporary associations or clumps. Light from the Sun strikes these clumps and is diffracted round them, but the diameter of a clump is much closer to the blue, short wavelength, end of the visible spectrum so the effect is very selective. This predominantly blue light from the SUN is diffracted round these molecular aggregations and appears to an observer to come from all parts of the sky.

The same process, but caused by larger particles suspended in the lower atmosphere, is responsible for sunrise and sunset colours.

Using light as an example; a beam of light travelling in one direction and meeting an obstacle will be diffracted into different beams which will cross over each other after the obstacle, leading to interference, another phenomenon shown by all wave motions. Two light beams of the same wavelength travelling in the same region of space interfere with each other; if they have the same AMPLITUDE and are out of PHASE, i.e., the crest of one lands on the trough of the other, they will cancel, giving a dark patch, destructive interference. If they are in PHASE, i.e., peak coinciding with peak, reinforcement occurs giving a bright patch, constructive interference. The combination of diffraction and INTERFERENCE gives rise to diffraction patterns, patches of light and shade with a form often related to the shape of the obstacle.

diffraction grating a useful instrument in astronomy which consists of thousands of closely spaced lines ruled on glass. Each line acts as a slit to incoming light, thus producing DIFFRACTION and interference and ultimately a diffraction pattern. Used in a spectrometer, the pattern is a spectrum with the light broken into its component wavelengths.

diffraction pattern *see* **diffraction**.

diffuse nebula *see* **nebula**.

diogenite a stony METEORITE lacking in CHONDRULES. It is composed of iron-rich pyroxene minerals.

Dione a satellite of SATURN, discovered by Cassini in 1684. One of eight large satellites, it has a diameter of 1,120km. The surface is heavily cratered in some regions but not in others, suggesting some recent activity. The density is low, 1,400kgm^{-3}, suggesting a mixture of ice and rock. The orbit is of radius 377,400km and the orbital PERIOD is 66 hours, almost exactly double that of Enceladus, another satellite of saturn. This is an example of an orbital RESONANCE.

dirty snowball model *see* **comet**.

disc galaxy *see* **galaxy**.

dispersion in light this refers to the variation of the refractive index of a substance with wavelength. For a prism, the refractive index is related to the angle through which the prism will bend or deviate a beam of light; thus a beam of white light incident on one face of a prism will emerge from another face as a fan of light, having the long, red, WAVELENGTHS deviated least and the short, blue, wavelengths most. The light has been broken up into its different wavelengths and presented in order, a SPECTRUM. A prism can be used as the dispersing element in a SPECTROMETER to allow the details of a spectrum to be examined. The spectrum produced by a DIFFRACTION grating has the colours in the reverse order.

dispersion measure A dispersion measure is a determination of how well a given prism or grating separates the wavelengths in, for example, a spectrometer.

displacement the distance moved by a particle or body in a given direction; a VECTOR quantity.

distance measurement within the solar system can be achieved by triangulation (*see* ANGULAR MEASURE) using the kilometre or ASTRONOMICAL UNIT as units. Few stars are sufficiently close for triangulation; but with the diameter of the Earth's orbit as base line a wider range is reached; the unit used is the PARSEC, or occasionally the LIGHT YEAR. Stars out to about 200 parsecs, or 6×10^{15}km, can be reached. Beyond this indirect methods, often involving statistical averages, are required. Rather over 20 GALAXIES have had their distances found, the limit being about 1 megaparsec, 10^6 parsec. Any type of VARIABLE STAR whose characteristics are known permits greater distances to be stepped out, e.g., a NOVA or rare SUPERNOVA. Further, by taking the apparent size and total light output of a whole galaxy or even a CLUSTER OF

GALAXIES it is possible to estimate the distance using statistical methods.

distance modulus *see* **distance measurement**.

distortion any reduction in the quality of an IMAGE, signal etc., brought about by instruments or apparatus handling it. In optics many LENS systems do not reproduce the exact form of the object correctly in the image e.g., barrel distortion occurs when the centre of the image is inflated and the outer edges bulge out, pincushion is the opposite effect.

diurnal happening every day, a recurrent event once in 24 hours.

diurnal motion movement taking place in the course of a day. The concept arises because of the spin of the Karth on its axis which makes CELESTIAL OBJECTS appear to move in the heavens. The motion of the Earth in its orbit round the sun is an additional factor.

diurnal parallax the apparent shift in position of a CELESTIAL OBJECT due to the rotation of the Earth.

Dog star Alpha Canis Majoris or SIRIUS.

Donati's Comet discovered in 1858, the coma produced a fountain effect as material spurted from the HEAD towards the Sun but was sprayed back by radiation and the SOLAR WIND.

Doppler effect an effect exhibited by all forms of WAVE MOTION. When the source of the wave and the observer are moving relative to each other the WAVELENGTH of the received radiation is reduced if source and observer are moving towards each other, and increased if moving apart. For light the relationship is $v = \frac{\Delta\lambda}{\lambda} C$ where v is the velocity which source and observer have relative to each other, is the wavelength of the light emitted, the change in wavelength and C the velocity of light. This is the origin of the REDSHIFT found in the recession of the galaxies. In one observation of a QUASAR it was found that a hydrogen line of wavelength 397nm, ordinarily in the ultra violet, had been redshifted to 463nm, in the blue region of the visible spectrum. Putting the figures into the equation gives $v = 5 \times 10^7 ms^{-1}$. In other words the quasar is moving away from us at about 16% of the velocity of light. Much higher redshifts have been detected.

Draco a northern sky constellation, near POLARIS the Pole Star; the brightest star in the constellation.

Draper classification a system of classifying stars by their spectrum based upon the HENRY DRAPER CATALOGUE of stars.

Dubhe Alpha Ursae Majoris, one of the POINTER STARS.

dust a name given to fine particles found throughout the universe, in the INTERPLANETARY MEDIUM where it gives rise to the ZODIACAL LIGHT; in the INTERSTELLAR MEDIUM where it gives rise to obscuring clouds and bands, markedly visible in GALAXIES seen edge on. In the shells surrounding exploded stars it can be rendered visible by light from stars and may be used to estimate the date of the explosion. A considerable mass is found in the form of dust throughout the universe.

dust tail the tail of a COMET is generally in two parts, a plasma tail and a dust tail. The latter is dust grains liberated from the nucleus as it evaporates in the Sun's radiation.

dwarf galaxy a smaller galaxy, usually elliptical, which contains perhaps one or two million times the mass of the Sun in a diameter of about 2000 parsec.

dwarf novae or cataclysmic variables are a class of VARIABLE STAR thought to be a very close BINARY STAR, where matter is being transferred from one component to the other.

dwarf star a normal star, found on the MAIN SEQUENCE of the

HERTZSPRUNG-RUSSELL DIAGRAM; the Sun is a fairly typical example although somewhat larger than the majority. The masses of dwarf stars cover the range from about one tenth to 60 times the Sun's mass and their life-span on the main sequence stage may range from a million years for a massive star to many thousands of millions of years for the lightest. Once the hydrogen burning phase in the core has completed, the star begins to evolve into some form of GIANT STAR and leaves the main sequence.

dynamical parallax a method of estimating the PARALLAX, and hence distance, of a binary star system. The observed orbits of the two stars around each other are established and the masses of the stars estimated using the MASS-LUMINOSITY relation; from these measurements the parallax can be estimated. It can be used for distances up to about 1000 parsec.

dynamical relating to any quantity involving motion.

E

Eagle Nebula an emission NEBULA in the constellation Seroens, 7000 light years away.

Earth the third planet out from the Sun of mass 5.977×10^{24}kg; it is roughly spherical, 12,756km diameter at the equator and 12,714km at the poles, the difference is caused by its spin. It is in an elliptical orbit with the Sun at one focus, from which it is distant 1.471×10^8km at PERIHELION and 1.521×10^8km at APHELION. With an average orbital speed of nearly 30kms⁻¹, it takes a year of 365¼ DAYS for one orbit. The spin axis is inclined at 23° 26′ to the orbital axis and this tilt is responsible for the seasons. There is an ATMOSPHERE extending to perhaps 1,000km and the atmospheric pressure at the surface is close to 1 BAR. Water vapour clouds are carried in the general circulation of the atmosphere, driven by the solar energy input of about 1.37kW m⁻². The crust varies from 6 to 40km in thickness, and land masses occupy just over 29%, the rest being water. The average DENSITY of the crust is 3,000kg m⁻³ whilst for the whole planet it is 5,000kg m⁻³, indicating denser material in deeper layers. A MAGNETIC FIELD reaches far out into space trapping charged particles which are stored in the VAN ALLEN BELTS; the field is probably created by fluid motions in the liquid layer. There is one natural satellite, the Moon, and gravitational effects from the Sun and Moon cause tides in the atmosphere, the oceans and even in the land mass.

eccentric a measure of how far an orbit, usually elliptical, departs from circular.

eccentricity *see* **ellipse**.

eclipse the passage of all (total eclipse) or part (partial eclipse) of a CELESTIAL BODY into the shadow cast by another thus blocking out the light from a third body. In a lunar eclipse, which can only occur at full moon, the shadow of the Earth cuts off the Sun's light from the Moon. In a solar eclipse, the Moon comes between the Sun and the Earth, casting a shadow over part of the Earth's surface. The diagram shows, not to scale, a solar eclipse.

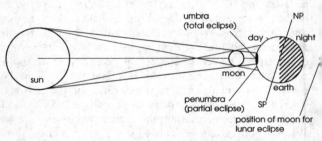

In the umbra, the eclipse is total, no part of the Sun can be seen from Earth; in the penumbra, the eclipse is partial and the Sun will be seen but with a circular edged region blocked by the Moon. As the Earth rotates on its axis, the zone of totality will appear to move over the surface; the Moon, however, is also in motion and quickly moves out of alignment (CONJUNCTION) so its shadow misses the Earth entirely. In the diagram, if the Moon were on the other side of the Earth, there would be a total eclipse of the Moon. Eclipses are comparatively rare events because the orbits of Earth round Sun and Moon round Earth are not quite in the same plane.

eclipsing binary a BINARY STAR system where one component periodically passes in front of the other as seen from Earth.

ecliptic the apparent path traced out by the Sun on the CELESTIAL SPHERE in the course of a year. It is only an apparent path since it is the Earth which orbits the Sun and the ecliptic can equally well be described as the circle marked on the celestial sphere by the extension of the plane of the Earth's orbit to cut the celestial sphere.

ecliptic coordinates the equivalent of longitude and latitude on Earth for finding the position of a CELESTIAL BODY on the CELESTIAL SPHERE based upon the ECLIPTIC in the celestial sphere.

Einstein outstanding physicist and mathematician who made great contributions to our understanding of the universe, particularly in his special, 1905, and general, 1915, THEORIES OF RELATIVITY. Amongst many other things he showed that the velocity of light in empty space was constant independent of the relative motion of source and observer; that mass and energy are equivalent and interchangeable, giving the mass-energy relationship $E = mc^2$ where E is the energy equivalent of mass m and c is the velocity of light; that both mass and dimensions of a body change with velocity. He showed also that space and time were linked and should be considered as one entity; that space could be curved and this curvature could be associated with gravity and that light was influenced by gravity. His ideas and the concepts to which they gave rise underlie most of modern physics and have a wide field of influence in astronomy and cosmology.

effective temperature the temperature an incandescent body would have, to give the same distribution of energy in its spectrum as a BLACK BODY would provide. Stars are not black body radiators and, in addition, the spectrum of a star usually contains absorption and emission lines which modify the spectrum. It is convenient, however, to match the star's spectrum to that of a black body at some specific temperature, thus giving the effective temperature of the star; it is a uniform way of defining the star's surface temperature and of finding the total energy output of the star. The Sun has an effective temperature of 5780K with an emission maximum in its spectrum at $5 \ 10^{-7}$m.

Elara a small, 76km diameter, satellite of JUPITER first observed in 1905. It is a member of a group of four small satellites having approximately the same orbits of radius just over 11,000kg and an orbital PERIOD close to 260 DAYS. The orbits are all similarly ECCENTRIC and considerably inclined to Jupiter's equator.

electricity a form of energy associated with the positions of electric charges (static electricity), or with their movements (current electricity). Currents cause, and are influenced by, magnetic fields. Accelerated charged particles give rise to the ELECTROMAGNETIC SPECTRUM of electromagnetic waves.

electromagnetic spectrum the continuous range of wavelengths and frequencies covered by ELECTROMAGNETIC WAVES. It is usually subdivided into smaller regions, as below, but these divisions are for convenience only, often based upon different methods of generation or detection, and do not represent any fundamental change in the nature of the radiated wave involved. The divisions are arbitrary and may overlap. For all electromagnetic waves $c=f$, where is the wavelength, f is the frequency and c is the velocity of light.

The 21 centimetre hydrogen LINE is an important feature

of RADIOASTRONOMY. Energy in eV gives the energy of a PHOTON of radiation of the specified wavelength, e.g., red light of wavelength 7 10^{-7}m can be considered as a stream of particles, photons, each of energy 1.78eV (*see* EMISSION LINE).

Different units are usually used for wavelengths in the different regions, e.g., visible light is almost always quoted in nanometres, 10^{-9}m, thus red light of wavelength 7 10^{-7}m is usually expressed as 700nm.

radiation	wavelength in m	frequency in Hz	energy in eV
gamma	$10^{16}\,10^{11}$	$3\,10^{24}\,3\,10^{19}$	$1.2\,10^{10}\,1.2\,10^{5}$
x-ray	$10^{-11}\,10^{-9}$	$3\,10^{19}\,3\,10^{17}$	$1.2\,10^{5}\,1.2\,10^{3}$
ultra-violet	$10^{-9}\,4\,10^{-7}$	$3\,10^{-17}\,7.5\,10^{14}$	$1.2\,10^{3}\,3.1$
visible	blue $4\,10^{-7}\,7$ 10^{-7} red	$7.5\,10^{-14}\,4.3$ 10^{14}	$3.1\,1.78$
infra-red	$7\,10^{-7}\,10^{-3}$	$4.3\,10^{14}\,3$ 10^{11}	$1.78\,1.2\,10^{-3}$
microwave	$10^{-3}\,1$	$3\,10^{11}\,3\,10^{5}$	$1.2\,10^{-3}\,1.2$ 10^{-9}
21cm Hydrogen line	.21	$1.4\,10^{9}$	$5.9\,10^{-6}$
radiowaves	$1\,10^{5}$	$3\,10^{5}\,3\,10^{3}$	$1.2\,10^{-9}\,1.2$ 10^{-11}

electromagnetic wave an electromagnetic wave is generated by a charged particle which is being accelerated. The wave consists of two wave motions, an electric field variation and a magnetic field variation at right angles to each other and advancing together through a space along the third perpendicular direction: the wave is a transverse wave, i.e., the oscillations are perpendicular to the direction of propagation, and the wave can travel through empty space, i.e., it does not need a medium in which to travel. The velocity of propagation in space is always the same, $c = 3 \times 10^8 \, \text{ms}^{-1}$ approximately, irrespective of any relative movement of the source or observer, i.e., the velocity of light is a constant. No body or particle can exceed the velocity of light and particles which are accelerated to speeds close to that of light exhibit RELATIVISTIC effects, e.g., relativity shows that the mass of a particle increases as it approaches the speed of light and its dimensions change.

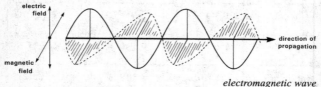

electromagnetic wave

electron a subatomic particle, constituent of all matter, which carries a charge of -1.6×10^{-19} Coulomb; has a very small mass, 9.11×10^{-31}kg and has a spin. In an atom there are as many electrons in the outer parts of the atom as there are protons in the nucleus and the atom is thus electrically neutral. The outermost electrons take part in chemical reactions. It is electrons, either bound to atoms or free, which respond to electromagnetic radiation. Ions are formed if one or more electrons are taken from or added to a neutral atom. Electrons are sufficiently light that they can be used most effectively to demonstrate the wave properties which are common to all matter and a beam of electrons can exhibit electron diffraction, i.e., form a diffraction pattern when passing an obstacle in the same way as light.

electron density the number of electrons per unit volume in a region of space.

electron volt the amount of kinetic energy possessed by an electron accelerated by a potential difference of 1 Volt., usually written as eV. $1eV = 1.6 \ 10^{-19}$ Joule. It is a convenient unit of energy when considering atomic processes.

element any one of the 92 different types of naturally occurring atoms which complete the periodic table and make up all matter in the universe. Artificially made transuranic elements, formed by exposing atoms to NEUTRONS from a nuclear pile, bring the number up to about 105, but all the artificially made elements are radioactive and decay, often rapidly, to less massive nuclei.

The elements of an orbit are the six quantities which are required to specify the orbit and the position in it of the orbiting body.

elementary particles the currently accepted collection of subatomic particles which are regarded as being the building blocks for all matter. For atoms, neutrons, protons and electrons were thought to be the elementary particles but it is now considered that neutrons and protons are formed from combinations of other particles called QUARKS. An elaborate scheme of elementary particles and anti-particles has been built up to explain observations or to suit the requirements of theory.

ellipse a CONIC SECTION, cut at an angle to the base. The ellipse has a high degree of symmetry, is like a flattened circle and has two foci. Most CELESTIAL BODIES are in elliptical orbits with the mass around which the body is in orbit situated at one focus. KEPLER'S LAWS describe the motion of a body in an elliptical orbit.

ellipticity a measure of how far an ELLIPSE deviates from a circle. It is the ratio of the length of one axis of symmetry over the other.

elliptical orbit *see* **ellipse.**

elliptical galaxy a GALAXY without spiral arms, it tends to have little in the way of dust clouds.

elongation the longitude angle, measured on the CELESTIAL SPHERE, between the position of the Moon, or a planet, and the position of the Sun at a particular time. For the inferior planets, Mercury and Venus, the greatest possible elongations are 28 and 48 respectively.

emersion the end of an ECLIPSE, when the eclipsed body is emerging from the shadow region.

emission the radiation of waves or particles; e.g., light from a source; heat from a body at a higher temperature than its surrounding's. Also alpha, beta or gamma rays from a radioactive source. The only information astronomers can get about CELESTIAL BODIES is by detecting and analysing their emissions.

emission line a line on a spectrum caused by a particular electronic transition in a specific atom. The electrons in atoms are arranged in specific energy levels determined by QUANTUM NUMBERS. In the normal state of the atom the electrons sit in the lowest energy level, the ground state. Energy in any form, but particularly light or electrical discharge, can excite one or more electrons temporarily to higher, empty, energy levels; the atom is then in an excited state. It subsequently relaxes and the excited electron drops from the upper level back to the ground state radiating the energy difference in the form of a PHOTON, a

bundle of light waves, a wave packet. The frequency of
the emitted light is given by the relationship $E = hf$, where
E is the energy difference, f is the frequency emitted and h
is a universal constant, Planck's constant. Thus a
transition between two particular energy levels always
results in a PHOTON of light of a particular frequency. Since
frequency, f, and wavelength, are related by f = c where c
is the velocity of light, this is equivalent to saying that a
given transition always gives radiation of the same
wavelength and is characteristic of that atom. A
spectrometer can be used to analyse the light from a
source, displaying it as a spectrum in which the range of
wavelengths is presented in order of wavelength. If the
source contains atoms excited as outlined above, then the
spectrum will have a bright emission line for each
particular electronic transition. Usually excited atoms
give off a number of different lines, perhaps a series,
which are characteristic of the atom, e.g., the Balmer
series for hydrogen. The presence of an emission
spectrum in the light from a star reveals the characteristic
"finger prints" of the atoms present.

An incandescent BLACK BODY does not give lines, instead
it gives a CONTINUOUS SPECTRUM but with a peak from
which the temperature of the black body can be found.
stars radiate to some extent as black bodies, thus would
give a continuous spectrum, but in the outer layers of
the Sun, for instance, is a cooler layer, the reversing
layer, where atoms at a considerably lower temperature
than the underlying PHOTOSPHERE are in a position to
absorb energy by the reverse of the process outlined. The
result is a continuous background spectrum crossed by
dark, FRAUNHOFER absorption lines, just as characteristic of
the atoms present.

emission nebula a NEBULA or cloud of dust and gas which is illuminated by the light from a very hot star, containing much ultra violet. This radiation can ionize the atoms in the nebula and thus generate EMISSION LINES in the spectrum. The light from the nebula thus contains the emitted light from the star, reflected by the dust and gas, along with bright emission lines superimposed. Emission excited in this way is often called LUMINESCENCE.

emission spectrum *see* **emission line.**

emissivity the efficiency with which a hot body radiates to its surroundings. A BLACK BODY radiates energy according to Stefan's law, $R = esT^4$, where R is the radiant energy in watts per square metre of its surface; s is Stefan's constant, about 6×10^{-8}; T is the surface temperature in K; and e is the emissivity which for a black body—a perfect radiator - is 1. For any object other than a black body, e has a value of less than 1; it is an indication of how near to a black body the surface of the radiator is.

The radiant energy, R, depends upon the fourth power of T, T^4, which means that if a body doubled its surface temperature, its radiant energy would increase by 16 times.

Enceladus a satellite of Saturn, discovered in 1789. It has a diameter of 500km and a density a little over that of water, suggesting that much of the satellite is made of ice. The ALBEDO, near to 1.0, is very high, higher even than for a fresh snowfall on Earth. There are cratered patches, but many regions of the surface are smooth and some have great ridges. It is likely that tidal effects from Saturn and other satellites, e.g., DIONE, have been responsible for generating energy within the satellite allowing the surface to flow. The orbit is near circular, 238,000km in radius, and not inclined.

Encke's comet the shortest known return period, 3.31 years, it has been seen 54 times.

energy the capacity for doing work. Broadly, two categories are recognized, kinetic and potential. Kinetic energy is thought of as stored in the movement of a body whilst potential energy is regarded as stored in the relative positions of bodies. Many different forms of energy are encountered, e.g., electricity, heat, wave motion, nuclear, chemical etc., and many ways of transporting energy are met with, electromagnetic waves, conduction, convection, etc. One feature common to all forms of energy, however, is that each may more or less readily be converted into another form. The work of EINSTEIN showed even mass to be a form of stored energy and that mass can be converted to other forms, e.g., heat, light, sound etc. Most sources of energy on Earth come eventually from the Sun; directly in the form of light and heat, indirectly in the movements of the atmosphere and as fossil fuels; the only supplementary source is from nuclear reactions.

Conservation of energy is illustrated by the motion of the Earth round the Sun, located at one focus of the ELLIPTICAL ORBIT. The Earth is closest to the Sun at PERIHELION, more distant at APHELION; to cause an increase in the distance between the two masses work has to be done against the gravitational attractions, and this work is stored in the system as an increase in potential energy. This increased potential energy is in turn drawn from the store of kinetic energy in the motion of the Earth, so the speed of the Earth in orbit changes. Thus, the Earth moves round its orbit at differing speeds, fastest at perihelion where potential energy has been exchanged for kinetic energy, slower at aphelion where the reverse takes place; but the total energy, the sum of kinetic and potential, remains the same at all times and in all places round the orbit. This varying rate of movement in the orbit causes the length of the day to vary slightly, represented as the equation of time. As a general principle, any system settles only when it has reached its lowest possible energy state.

ephemeris a table or ALMANAC giving the future positions of Sun, Moon, planets, stars etc. Useful for navigators and astronomers. The Nautical Almanac of the Royal Greenwich Observatory is an example.

Epimetheus a satellite of Saturn. A small irregular body, it is in virtually the same orbit as Janus, 151,420km radius. They may both originally have come from one large body.

epoch much astronomical information is valid only at a particular time due to the motions of the bodies involved; such data is presented along with the epoch, the time for which it was valid.

equation of time because the earth is in an elliptical orbit, its speed round the orbit changes causing the length of the day—as found from atomic clocks—to vary. An imaginary object, the mean sun, is therefore considered whose motion on the CELESTIAL SPHERE is uniform, i.e., the mean sun is assumed to be at the centre of a circular orbit for the Earth, and the equation of time represents the time difference between the real Sun and the mean sun. During a year the two can differ by up to 16 minutes. The time as measured by the mean sun is called mean solar time and the day length as the mean solar day.

equator the great circle on a CELESTIAL BODY that is equidistant from the poles. A plane perpendicular to the axis of rotation of the body and through its centre would cut the surface at the equator. The CELESTIAL EQUATOR is defined as the line traced out on the CELESTIAL SPHERE by the extension of the plane defining the Earth's equator to reach the celestial sphere.

equatorial coordinates *see* **celestial sphere**.

equatorial mounting a telescope mounting in which one axle is aligned in the same direction as the Earth's spin axis, the other axle is perpendicular to it. If the telescope is sighted on a star, then to counteract the drift in apparent position of the star caused by the Earth's rotation, a counter rotation about the former axis is all that is required for many purposes. This can be arranged by some form of clock drive.

equinox *see* **ecliptic**.

Eridanus a CONSTELLATION of considerable size running from the CELESTIAL EQUATOR well into the southern sky. The brightest star, Alpha Eridiani is also known as ACHERNAR.

Eros a small ASTEROID, one of the AMOR group. It spends most of its time inside the orbit of Mars and comes close to the Earth.

escape velocity the minimum velocity that any body must have in order to escape entirely from the gravitational force of another body. If the mass of a celestial body is too low, for instance, then the gravitational force is too weak to hold onto the molecules of an atmosphere, thus many smaller bodies, e.g., the Moon, have no atmosphere. The escape velocity for the Moon is 2.4kms^{-1} and for the Earth 11.2kms^{-1}.

Eta Carinae a VARIABLE star in the constellation CARINA. In 1843 it suddenly brightened to become the second brightest in the sky after SIRIUS, but relapsed back to be about 6th magnitude and thus barely visible to the unaided eye. It is thought to be an unstable SUPERGIANT which may possibly become a SUPERNOVA. It lies in the Keyhole

Nebula, NGC3372 a dark nebula of dust embedded in a bright nebula.

Eta Carina Nebula *see* **Eta Carinae**.

eucrite a coarse grained rock with large pyroxene crystals. The name was given in 1863 to STONY METEORITES of this composition (*see also* ACHONDRITE).

Europa the smallest of the four Galilean satellites of Jupiter, discovered in 1610 by Galileo; with a diameter of 3,138km. The DENSITY is quite high, nearly 3,000kgm^{-3}, suggesting it is largely rock, although the surface appears to be icy and not heavily cratered. The orbit is nearly circular of radius 670,900km and is in the plane of Jupiter's equator. Europa lies between IO and GANYMEDE and they have closely related orbital periods.

European Space Agency ESA, a cooperative venture in space research and technology established in 1975 with headquarters in Paris, in which fifteen countries participate. The ARIANE rocket launching system is used to put satellites in orbit, amongst others Giotto the planetary probe that intercepted HALLEY'S COMET.

evening star a popular name for a planet, usually VENUS, although MERCURY shows similar effects, which appears in the western sky at or just after sunset. The same phenomenon seen just before sunrise has the name morning star.

event horizon *see* **black hole**.

evolution change with time in an ordered manner, e.g., the study of stellar evolution follows the life history of a star from formation, through all its changes in form and structure, to its final state. Similarly, the BIG BANG theory allows the study of the development of the universe from its formation up to its present stage and seeks to predict its future.

expanding universe *see* **cosmology.**

expansion of the universe *see* **cosmology.**

extinction the reduction in intensity of light or other radiation by absorption, scattering etc. Measurement of all magnitudes of stars is affected by extinction in the Earth's atmosphere and light from any star may suffer extinction by INTERSTELLAR DUST.

eyepiece in an optical instrument, the lens or lens system to which the eye of the observer applies his eye. It is used to magnify the image formed by the primary mirror or lens and for observational purposes may have crosswires or other measurement devices incorporated.

F

Fabry-Perot interferometer a very high RESOLUTION device for examining the fine structure of spectral lines, often used along with a SPECTROMETER. It consists of two flat transparent plates, partially silvered on their inner surfaces. They are clamped strictly parallel with a small air gap enclosed. Light from the required source enters through one plate and is reflected to and fro between the plates. Only wavelengths which 'fit' exactly into the distance separating the plates experience constructive INTERFERENCE many times and emerge as a very sharp spectral line in the form of a ring pattern, with fine structure resolved. The resolution is so high that only a very limited part of the spectrum can be examined at one time, so a spectrometer is used to examined a particular line.

faculae bright granular structure of the Sun's surface caused by hotter regions on the PHOTOSPHERE. They are associated with SUNSPOTS, are regions of strengthened magnetic field and their influence extends up into the CHROMOSPHERE.

F corona the outermost region of the Sun's CORONA.

field of view the area in an optical telescope on the CELESTIAL SPHERE, or any large body, e.g., the Moon, which is in view at any one time through the eyepiece. This has been broadened to include radio-telescopes and gamma-ray telescopes, but the definition is the same.

field curvature a lens ABERRATION or optical defect in which, over the field of view, only the central region is in sharp focus, the outer sections being brought to a focus in a slightly different plane; it is as if the image was formed on a curved surface.

filament a fine thread-like feature seen on the Sun's surface particularly in the PENUMBRA of a SUNSPOT associated with a gas flow.

filar micrometer a set of very fine crosswires which can be moved by a sensitive micrometer screw gauge. They are often fitted to a telescope in such a way that they are in focus in the same plane as the image when viewed through the eyepiece, so that after calibration measurements of distances across the image can be made.

filter (optics) a device which allows a limited range of the ELECTROMAGNETIC SPECTRUM to pass through. One form is a sheet of plastic material with dyes incorporated to block certain wavelength ranges. Others rely on the interference of light to select only a very narrow width of the SPECTRUM. They are basically the same as the FABRY-PEROT INTERFEROMETER but have the space between the partially silvered plates filled with a solid transparent material. They can be made sufficiently selective so that only a very narrow spectrum is passed, e.g., centred on the red emission line H at 656.3nm. A photograph taken of a region of the CELESTIAL SPHERE through such a filter would reveal, principally, stars with strong hydrogen emission lines. The results would require careful interpretation, however, because stars in motion towards or away from the observer might have the hydrogen line shifted by the DOPPLER EFFECT beyond the pass band of the filter.

finder a smaller telescope with a wide field of view rigidly attached to a larger instrument to assist in locating CELESTIAL OBJECTS. A powerful telescope has a very narrow field of view and it is often difficult to locate a specific object. The finder has a much wider field of view and is so adjusted that if the required celestial body coincides with its reference crosswires, then it will appear near the centre of the field in the main telescope.

first quarter a particular phase of the Moon when it is seen as exactly half illuminated, the limit to the illuminated area appearing as a straight line.

fission the process by which a heavy nucleus splits into two lighter fragments with the release of energy. It is a natural process, but can be stimulated by irradiation with charged particles in which case it is called induced fission. The energy release is accompanied by a loss of mass, the mass has been converted to energy as illustrated in the Einstein mass-energy equation. In a fission reaction; as well as the two daughter nuclei into which the heavy nucleus splits, several NEUTRONS are released, if arrangements are made to allow these to be captured by another fissile nucleus, a chain reaction occurs. A controlled chain reaction is the power source of a nuclear reactor.

fixed star stars at such a great distance that they have no detectable PARALLAX due to Earth's movement in its orbit. Such stars, as seen on the CELESTIAL SPHERE, appear to be fixed in position throughout the year whereas nearer stars appear to move in a regular way. Allowance has to be made for PRECESSION. Many nearer stars also exhibit PROPER MOTION, i.e., their movement through space, this can be distinguished from parallax as the star does not return to the same position at the end of a year.

flare a disturbance in the upper CHROMOSPHERE of the Sun apparently in the form of a flame. It may be accompanied by the emission of increased numbers of charged particles, protons, electrons and ions, which have enough energy to reach Earth and interact with the magnetic field, causing geomagnetic storms, and with the upper atmosphere, causing AURORAE.

flare star or U.V. Ceti stars, named after their prototype are explosive VARIABLE stars which in a few seconds may increase their brightness by several magnitudes, returning to their former state in a few tens of minutes. They are mostly cool MAIN SEQUENCE yellow or red stars similar to the Sun, but the nature of the flare seems to be different. It may be that they convey heat from the core to the surface purely by convection.

flash spectrum a line SPECTRUM of the limb of the Sun taken just before or just after totality in an ECLIPSE of the sun. The thin crescent, consisting only of the atmosphere of the sun gives a line spectrum from which the elements present in the solar atmosphere may be found.

Flora group a family of asteroids which have more or less identical orbits, about 2.2 astronomical units radius. Only one member of any size.

focus the point to which rays of light converge when passed through an optical system. The focus, or focal point, for a lens or a concave mirror, is the point on the axis of the lens or mirror to which a parallel beam of light directed along the axis will converge. Provided the parallel beam does not make too great an angle with the axis (paraxial rays), the focus represents the place where the focal plane, a plane perpendicular to the axis and on which the focus always lies, cuts the axis. In a telescope the objective, lens or mirror, accepts parallel light from distant CELESTIAL BODIES in the field of view and brings it to a focus, forming an image of the bodies in the focal plane, this image is then examined by the eye piece.

One of the two symmetrical points on the major axis of

an elliptical orbit where the more massive body, e.g., the Sun, may be situated whilst the lighter body, the Earth traces out the orbit.

focal length a beam of parallel light directed along the axis toward a concave mirror is reflected by the mirror and converges to a point, the FOCUS, on the axis. The focal length of the mirror is the distance measured from the pole of the mirror, where the axis meets the reflecting surface, to the focus. A similar definition can be given for a "thin" lens, i.e., one where the thickness of the glass is negligible, but for real lenses and in particular lens systems, the situation is more complex.

focal plane *see* **focus**.

Fomalhaut (Alpha Piscis Austrini) a 1st MAGNITUDE hot DWARF STAR. There is a disc of cool material present which may possibly be forming planets.

forbidden lines when an EMISSION LINE is formed in an emission spectrum, it is caused by an electron making a transition from a higher energy level to a lower one and radiating the energy difference as a PHOTON. Some transitions are, however, 'forbidden', in the sense that an electron making that drop would change QUANTUM NUMBERS in a way which cannot normally happen. In conditions obtaining in some NEBULAE, however, spectral lines due to such transitions are found. At first it was thought they were due to an unknown element which was given the name "nebulium". Subsequently it was realised that certain factors allowed these very unlikely transitions to take place in sufficient numbers to give a strong spectral line where none was expected.

force that which, when acting on a body free to move, causes an acceleration of the body. It is related to the mass of the body, m, and the acceleration of the body, a, by the equation Force = m a. Force is a VECTOR quantity. When a force F moves a distance d in its own direction, work is done where Work = F d. Work is not a vector quantity.

Forbush effect an occasional decrease in the intensity of cosmic rays at times when SOLAR FLARES are prominent, possibly associated with the coincident magnetic fields.

Fornax a southern sky constellation, no stars brighter than the 4th magnitude. It contains the Fornax System, a dwarf ELLIPTICAL GALAXY which is a member of the LOCAL GROUP of galaxies. It also contains the Fornax cluster, one of the nearest CLUSTERS OF GALAXIES.

Foucault's pendulum a pendulum consisting of a very heavy bob suspended from a very long wire and set in motion in a particular plane. The pendulum remains in this plane, in space, whilst the Earth rotates beneath it; it therefore demonstrates the rotation of the Earth. It would give a maximum effect if set up at one of the poles, zero effect at the equator.

Fraunhofer lines dark lines crossing the CONTINUOUS SPECTRUM of the Sun caused by a relatively cooler layer, the REVERSING LAYER, above the PHOTOSPHERE where atoms absorb light from the continuous spectrum. It is an ABSORPTION SPECTRUM in the form of SPECTRAL LINES.

frequency the number of vibrations per second of any periodic phenomenon. The unit is the Hertz, Hz. For all waves, wavelength , frequency f and velocity of propagation v are related by the equation $f = v$. For sound, v is about $330 ms^{-1}$ so a frequency of 264Hz corresponds to a wavelength of 1.25m. For light, or any other part of the ELECTROMAGNETIC SPECTRUM, the velocity of light is near to $3 \ 10^8 ms^{-1}$ so a frequency of 264Hz corresponds to a wavelength of 1.25m.

F star *see* **spectral classification**.

full moon a particular PHASE of the Moon when it is seen as exactly fully illuminated.

fundamental constant a number of quantities which occur in all science appear to have particular importance and generality, the values of such quantities appear always to be the same; such quantities are called fundamental constants. A few are given here:

velocity of light in vacuum	2.997925	$10^8 ms^{-1}$
charge on an electron	1.602192	$10^{-19}C$
Planck's constant	6.62620	$10^{-34}JS$
gravitational constant	6.673	$10^{-11}Nm^2kg^{-2}$
mass of an electron at rest	9.10956	$10^{-31}kg$
mass of proton at rest	1.672614	$10^{-27}kg$
mass of neutron at rest	1.674920	$10^{-27}kg$

fundamental particles *see* **elementary particles**.

fusion reaction a NUCLEAR REACTION in which the nuclei of light elements are fused together to make heavier elements with loss of mass and consequent release of energy.

G

galactic centre the centre of the MILKY WAY GALAXY. As seen from Earth, the galactic centre lies in the direction of the constellation Sagittarius.

galactic coordinates a coordinate system using ANGULAR MEASURE to specify the position of any object or point in the MILKY WAY GALAXY in which the solar system lies. The Milky Way Galaxy, or just Galaxy, is a collection of about a hundred thousand million, 10^{11}, stars of which the Sun is a member. The galaxy is in the form of a flattened disk with a central nucleus, containing a large assembly of stars, round which other stars are arranged in a pattern of flattened spiral arms winding round the nucleus and lying in a plane, the Galactic plane. Much absorbing dust lies in the spaces between the stars and congregates particularly in the Galactic plane. If the galaxy could be seen edge on it would appear in simplified form as in the diagram:

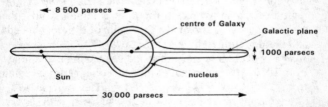

Thus looking from Earth in any direction along the Galactic plane the appearance should be of an irregular, narrow, bright band of stars which would appear in a circle across the celestial sphere. This is what is known as the Milky Way. The thick dust tends to obscure stars exactly in the Galactic plane, so the narrow bright band of the Milky Way has an irregular dark lane down the centre, splitting it.

The plane of the Galaxy is an imaginary plane through the centre and symmetrically through the thickness of the spiral arms.

galactic halo the large spherical volume surrounding the Galaxy containing old POPULATION II stars and globular clusters. The halo also contains a magnetic field and highly ionized gas at ahigh temperature. The source of heat may be supernova explosions.

galactic nucleus the assembly of stars at the centre of the GALAXY and similar spirals. They are typically old POPULATION II STARS; there may be a BLACK HOLE.

galactic plane *see* **galactic coordinates**.

galactic poles *see* **galactic coordinates**.

galactic rotation the PROPER MOTIONS of stars in the GALAXY show that they are in orbit around the galactic nucleus. Spectroscopic studies of nearby galaxies, using the DOPPLER EFFECT, show that their outer stars are in rotation also about their galactic nucleus. The stars in the central region of a galaxy tend to rotate in common, whilst the stars of the spiral arms have the orbits of different speeds and period required by KEPLER'S LAWS.

galaxy a collection of stars, dust and gas having a total mass from 10^6 to 10^{13} times that of the Sun contained in a region from 2000 to 60,000 PARSECS across. They appear to be arranged in aggregations called CLUSTERS with a few members to several thousand. Hubble classified galaxies into three classes according to their obvious visible features, ELLIPTICAL, SPIRAL and barred spiral and also a group of irregulars. Elliptical galaxies range from the almost spherical to the very flattened lens-shaped, E0 to E7. Typically they are made up of older POPULATION II stars and hot gas but have little dust and range from dwarf elliptical to the largest known galaxies of all, the massive CD type, which tend to lie at the centres of the largest clusters. Spiral galaxies are in the form of a flattened disk with a central nucleus containing a large assembly of stars, mainly older POPULATION II, round which other stars are arranged in a pattern of flattened spiral arms winding round the nucleus and lying in a plane (SO and Sa to Sc in Hubble's classification). The majority of stars are in the arms and are younger POPULATION I stars and there is much dust as well as gas in the INTERSTELLAR medium. The barred spirals are similar in most ways to the spirals, but have a bar structure across the nucleus from the ends of which the spiral arms emerge. SBO to Sbc in Hubble's classification. The nearest galaxy to the Milky Way, the LARGE MAGELLANIC CLOUD, may be a barred spiral. Irregular galaxies range from those with little apparent structure, like the SMALL MAGELLANIC CLOUD which may be very young, to the highly structured CARTWHEEL GALAXY (*see also* MARKARIAN GALAXIES, N-TYPE GALAXIES, SEYFERT GALAXIES).

Distance measurements to galaxies have been made by the use of CEPHEID VARIABLES for nearer galaxies and by statistical methods for those more distant. In general galaxies appear to be receding from us, the velocity of recession being found from the DOPPLER SHIFT of SPECTRAL LINES, the RED SHIFT.

Galaxy the Milky Way Galaxy, (*see* GALACTIC COORDINATES and GALAXY). The centre of the Galaxy may contain a

BLACK HOLE and does have a strong radio source, SAGITTARIUS A.

Galilean satellites the four satellites of Jupiter first observed by Galileo in 1610; IO, EUROPA, GANYMEDE and CALLISTO.

Galilean telescope a refracting, i.e., one using LENSES only, TELESCOPE invented by Galileo Galilei. The front lens brings light from a distant source to a focus in the FOCAL PLANE. The second lens is placed nearer the objective than its focal plane and enables a magnified image to be seen. The system is still in use today in simple opera glasses since it gives an image the correct way up and with a short length instrument.

gamma the third letter in the Greek alphabet. As a BAYER letter, it denotes the third brightest star in a CONSTELLATION.

gamma ray an electromagnetic wave of short WAVELENGTH and high energy. It is a product of many nuclear reactions as well as of natural radioactivity (*see* ELECTROMAGNETIC SPECTRUM).

gamma-ray astronomy the study of GAMMA RAYS produced by natural processes anywhere in the universe. It is a new field of study made possible in the main by artificial satellites as most gamma rays from space interact with atoms in the atmosphere.

gamma-ray bursts rapid fluctuations in the output of gamma rays from a source. First noticed in the late 1960s, over 30 are now known. The fluctuation in intensity can be very rapid, a few milliseconds to a few tens of seconds, which suggests a small source, perhaps a PULSAR.

Ganymede a satellite of Jupiter discovered by Galileo in 1610. It is the largest satellite in the solar system and at 5,262kg diameter it is bigger than the planet Mercury (4,878km diameter). It has a heavily cratered surface and brighter areas of more recent formation crossed by grooves and faults. The density, 1,940kgm⁻³, suggests a mixture of ice and rock. It is in a nearly circular orbit, of radius 1,070 ¥ 10⁶km, round the planet's equator. EUROPA, Ganymede and CALLISTO have orbital periods which are closely related.

gas cloud an isolated accumulation of gas, often with dust mixed through, occurring throughout the K. Some clouds are rendered visible as NEBULAE which may be bright, shining by LUMINESCENCE, or simply illuminated by nearby stars, or dark and thus obscuring light. There is evidence of star formation in gas clouds or BOK GLOBULES (*see also* GALAXY,GRAVITATIONAL COLLAPSE).

Gemini zodiacal constellation, between CANCER and TAURUS at 7 hour right ascension and 22north declination. The two brightest stars are POLLUX and CASTER, Beta Geminorum and Alpha Geminorum respectively. The constellation lies at the edge of the MILKY WAY.

geocentre having the earth as centre (*see also* COPERNICAN SYSTEM).

geocorona the outermost part of Earth's atmosphere, extending out to about 15 earth-radii. It consists mainly of a halo of hydrogen which is emissive, by luminescence, when exposed to solar radiation.

geodesy the surveying of the Earth on a large scale in which the surface curvature becomes important.

geomagnetic field the magnetic field of the Earth, almost certainly caused by motion in the fluid core. The field is rather like that from a small bar magnet, but is not exactly aligned along the Earth's rotation axis and is affected locally by magnetic deposits. The field extends into space and interacts with the SOLAR WIND to form the magnetosphere. It serves to trap charged particles, as in the VAN ALLEN radiation belts, and to direct incoming charged particles to polar regions where they are responsible for AURORAE.

geomagnetic storm a disturbance of the interaction of the Earth's magnetic field in the magnetosphere with incoming charged particles, often a result of a solar FLARE.

geosynchronous *or* **geostationary orbit** a body, e.g. a satellite, put into a geosynchronous orbit should have a period of exactly one day and thus rotate with the Earth appearing to be stationary vertically above one point on the surface. Because the Earth is not a perfect sphere, and from other imperfections, corrections have to be made to the orbit of such a satellite in order to keep it geostationary.

giant plant JUPITER, SATURN, NEPTUNE and URANUS have much greater masses and diameters than the other planets. Jupiter and Saturn together make up over 90% of the mass of the planetary system. Together they are referred to as giant planets.

giant star stars which have evolved considerably and have 'burnt' the hydrogen of the core to form helium, expand their outer layers and become giant stars with diameters up to a hundred times that of the Sun. Many of the brightest stars are giants e.g., ALDEBARAN, CAPELLA and POLLUX. Some giant stars become VARIABLE e.g., RR LYRA and MIRA CETI classes. On the HERTZ SPRUNG-RUSSELL diagram giant stars have evolved away from the MAIN SEQUENCE to the upper right.

globular cluster *see* **star cluster**.

Gould's Belt also known as the Local System, this is an assemblage of young, hot, blue POPULATION I STARS in the MILKY WAY. As well as the stars there are copious quantities of gas and dust in the region. The oldest stars in the Belt and the rate of expansion of the region suggest that the stars were born under a hundred million years ago, but there is no agreement as to the cause.

granulation *see* **convection zone**.

gravitation the name given to the effect of the force of gravity which exists between masses. Newton's law of gravitation is given in mathematical form as the force F between any two masses M_1 and M_2 whose centres are a distance R apart is given by $F=G\frac{M_1M_2}{R_2}$ where G, the gravitational constant, 6.673×10^{-11} Nm^2kg^{-2}, is a universal FUNDAMENTAL CONSTANT. The force appears to be always one of attraction and the relationship to hold over the whole universe, although in the BRANS-DICKE theory the value of G is assumed to change with time. KEPLER'S LAWS of PLANETARY motion are a consequence of Newton's law.

Gravitation is classified as a weak force but the vast masses in the universe give rise to such very large scale forces that they are of great significance in cosmology. Newton's law of gravitation holds over a very wide range, but EINSTEIN's theory of GENERAL RELATIVITY must be used where very strong gravitational forces obtain.

gravitational attraction *see* **gravitation**.

gravitational collapse the force of gravity acts throughout the universe and any one mass is drawn to all other masses. When masses can collapse together, a lower energy state results and released energy transformed, usually into heat. Further, the GRAVITATIONAL FORCE is directed inwards to the centre of each mass. Reflecting this directional symmetry CELESTIAL BODIES are generally spherical.

Any gas cloud in space will collapse under its own gravity. The contraction compresses the central volume of gas and, as it is an ADIABATIC PROCESS, the released energy heats it. Where the mass of gas is great enough and its materials suitable, the hot compressed core may ignite in a nuclear FUSION reaction, and a star is born. The escape of the released energy from the reaction prevents further gravitational collapse. If the temperature and pressure of the core do not become high enough, ignition can not take place; Jupiter may represent such a class of body, a BROWN STAR, which has failed to generate nuclear energy. Eventually the nuclear fuel will burn away, energy will cease to be generated and gravitational collapse resume, perhaps to give a NEUTRON STAR or even a BLACK HOLE. Should the mass of material in the universe be great enough, the current expansion against the decelerating force of gravity will come to a halt, to be replaced by gravitational collapse.

gravitational instability a situation in which bodies acted on by GRAVITY are in a stable position with respect to each other, but where a slight displacement destroys the stability. EINSTEIN developed his relativity theories to produce models of the universe, all proved to be gravitationally unstable, i.e., a slight displacement was followed by transformation from a stable configuration into an expanding or a contracting universe.

gravitational lens in Einstein's theory of RELATIVITY it is shown that light is affected by GRAVITATION, e.g., a ray of light is deflected on coming under a strong gravitational field, an effect which was observed at the solar eclipse of 1919. Applied to radiation received from a very distant source, it is possible that if some very massive, but small, object lay in the line of sight the radiation might bend round the mass and in a way rather like a lens, concentrate or focus the radiation, thus giving a false impression of its intensity.

gravitational redshift in EINSTEIN'S general theory of RELATIVITY it is shown that light is affected by GRAVITATION. One consequence is that light loses energy in moving away from a massive body. Loss of energy by a photon corresponds to a lower frequency and longer wavelength, so light coming from a massive body will have a longer wavelength, i.e., be shifted to the red.

gravitational waves in EINSTEIN'S general theory of RELATIVITY it is shown that space and time cannot be considered separately but as a combined quantity SPACE-TIME in which a gravitational wave would travel with the velocity of light (gravitational radiation). It would be very difficult to detect and only some major cosmic occurrence, e.g., the sudden collapse of a star, would produce a concentrated source of gravitational waves which could be detected.

great circle any circle, e.g. the CELESTIAL EQUATOR, drawn on the CELESTIAL SPHERE.

Great Dark Spot an atmospheric feature on NEPTUNE, possibly a whirling dust storm, situated in the southern hemisphere.

Great Red Spot an atmospheric feature on JUPITER first discovered by Hooke (1664). It moves in longitude but remains fixed in latitude just over 23 south of the planet's equator. An infra red light study shows that it is a cold high pressure region in Jupiter's atmosphere, similar to an anticyclone on Earth. Various suggestions have been put forward for the colour, ranging from ammonia to phosphorus.

greenhouse effect an effect of the Earth's atmosphere. Relatively short wavelength solar radiation, visible light, can travel through the atmosphere largely unhindered because of an ATMOSPHERIC WINDOW at these wavelengths.

This short wavelength radiation is mainly absorbed at the surface of the Earth causing heating. The amount of energy received this way is considerable, it is called the SOLAR CONSTANT and amounts to 1.37kWm^{-2}. The Earth is a relatively cool body, but even so the only way it can lose heat is by radiation to outer space. For a body at the temperature of the Earth, about 300K, the BLACK BODY radiation curve has an emission peak far into the infra red where there is no atmospheric window, the water vapour and especially carbon dioxide in the atmosphere are highly absorbing at these wavelengths. Thus much of the incoming solar radiation is retained on the Earth's surface and in the atmosphere causing the temperature to rise and avoids extremes of heat and cold. The growing concentration of gases such as carbon dioxide causes global warming. The name 'greenhouse effect' comes into being because the glass in a greenhouse has a very similar effect, it is transparent to short wavelength solar radiation but absorbs strongly at long waves in the infra red.

Greenwich Mean Time (G.M.T.) also known as Universal Time (U.T.). The mean solar time defined on the GREENWICH MERIDIAN. LOCAL TIME is based on GMT by allowing 1 hour for every 15 of longitude east (ahead) or west (behind) Greenwich. The time scale now in use is based on the standards of the ATOMIC CLOCK, but the two times are kept together by frequent adjustment.

Greenwich Meridian the imaginary line drawn over the surface of the Earth from pole to pole which cuts the equator at right angles and passes through a particular point at the Royal Greenwich Observatory. This is taken as the zero of longitude and all angular measure of longitude starts from this zero meridian.

Gregorian Calendar *see* **calendar**.

Gregorian telescope a type of telescope invented by James Gregory (1638-75) of Drumoak. The first practical reflecting telescope.

G star a star of characteristics like the Sun.

guide telescope *see* **finder**.

Gum nebula the largest known NEBULA, located in the southern constellations Puppis and Vela. It is a complex of diffuse glowing gas, possibly the remnants of an ancient SUPERNOVA explosion.

H

Hadar *see* **Beta Centauri**.

Hale telescope the 200-inch telescope at Mount Palomar Observatory. It took fifteen years to build and regular observing began in 1949. In common with most ground-based telescopes it is seldom able to be used to full effect because of ABSORPTION by, and distortion from, movements in EARTH'S ATMOSPHERE.

Halley's comet the first known periodic COMET. Halley was ASTRONOMER ROYAL 1720–1742 and a contemporary of Newton. He applied Newton's methods of calculating cometary orbits to a number of recorded sightings and realised that comets seen in 1531, 1607 and 1682 had very similar orbits and were from a periodic comet, the first known. It had been recorded as far back as AD 374 and was embroidered on the Bayeux Tapestry as it had been seen in 1066. Halley did not live to see the 1759 return he had predicted. It returns to the inner part of the solar system about every 76 years, orbiting the Sun in the opposite direction to the planets, and at PERIHELION is 0.59 ASTRONOMICAL UNITS from the Sun. The orbit stretches well beyond Neptune. The nucleus is now about 11km diameter and it loses about 0.1% of its mass at every return. Dust particles left in the orbit give rise to two METER SHOWERS, the Eta Aquarid shower in late April and the Orionids in late October.

halo a name used for a considerable number of optical

phenomena. The word essentially means a circle of white or coloured light surrounding a body, as such it is used with reference to COMETS, GLOBULAR CLUSTERS and GALAXIES amongst others. A particular use of the term is to describe a ring or ring system seen surrounding the Sun or Moon, especially in the presence of faint, high cirrus clouds. This halo, which may be coloured, is at an angular radius of about 22° and is formed by REFRACTION through ice crystals in the cloud.

Hamal *see* **Alpha Arietis (Aries).**

h and Persei NGC869 and NGC884, twin open STAR CLUSTERS in PERSEUS. They are both visible to the unaided eye and appear to have evolved from the same GAS CLOUD as the stars in both clouds are young and very similar. They belong to the MILKY WAY, lying at the end of one of the spiral arms.

Hawking effect connected with BLACK HOLES. The term black hole implies that nothing, no matter, no radiation, could ever escape from it. Hawking showed that this was not the case and that particles could escape from black holes and, further, in a two stage process happening in the neighbourhood of a black hole, matter-ANTI MATTER pairs could be created with the antimatter entering the black hole and the matter particle escaping, thus reducing the mass of the black hole and, effectively, radiating matter from it. As Hawking expressed it, 'Black holes ain't so black'.

Hayashi track (*or* line) a particular path on the HERTZSPRUNG–RUSSELL diagram which it is thought represents the evolution of a young star as it joins the MAIN SEQUENCE. It would represent a short period in the life of a star and thus not many stars are likely to be found on this path.

head *see* **comet.**

Hektor *or* **Hector** an ASTEROID, a member of one of the two groups of asteroids which are in the same orbit as Jupiter round the Sun, known as the TROJAN GROUP. Hektor shows considerable magnitude changes in its orbit and it is thought it might be a binary system of two associated asteroids.

heliacal rising the rising of a star or planet which is visible just before sunrise; if the rising of the sun and the star or planet are too close, then the Sun's dazzling illumination prevents the fainter body being seen. The heliacal rising of SIRIUS was used by the ancient Egyptians as an indicator of the coming annual rise of the Nile.

heliacal setting the setting of a star or planet coinciding with sunrise.

heliocentric system *see* **Copernican system**.

heliocentric a coordinate system in which the positions and velocities of all objects in the solar system are referred to the centre of the Sun as origin.

heliosphere a large region surrounding the Sun where the SOLAR WIND predominates; it is some 50 to 100 ASTRONOMICAL UNITS from the Sun and the somewhat uncertain boundary, the heliopause, is taken to be where the solar wind is becoming indistinguishable from the interstellar wind.

heliostet *see* **ceolostat**.

helium the second lightest element, after hydrogen. Helium has a NUCLEUS of two PROTONS and two NEUTRONS and thus two ELECTRONS in orbit. The two electrons fill all the immediately available energy levels and thus form a complete shell, hence helium is chemically very unreactive. The NUCLEUS is an ALPHA PARTICLE when emitted with high velocity from a RADIOACTIVE disintegration; it is too interactive to have great penetrating power, but leaves

a track of heavily ionized material behind it. It is common
in the universe, something like one third of the total mass
is helium, most of that being formed within a few minutes
of the BIG BANG. Helium was first recognized in the
FRAUNHOFER LINES in the Sun's spectrum. Along with
hydrogen it forms the bulk of the Sun's mass; the energy
of the Sun comes from NUCLEAR FUSION REACTIONS in which
hydrogen nuclei are fused to form helium.

Helium remains a gas down to low temperatures, 4.2K,
and it is therefore a convenient refrigerant for low
temperature work. It can be used in this form to cool
detectors which are used in astronomical observations;
this is desirable to cut down thermal noise in the
instruments.

helium flash a late stage in the life history of a star. A star of
about the size of the Sun after spending most of its life on
the MAIN SEQUENCE of the HERTZSPRUNG-RUSSELL DIAGRAM,
moves up and to the right as a GIANT star then down and
left to remain above the main sequence, often as a
VARIABLE STAR. During this latter journey the core collapses
giving rise to temperatures of $100 \ 10^6$K at which nuclear
fusion reactions can occur, burning helium to form
CARBON; this is known as the helium flash. The star quickly
burns the helium and eventually journeys across the main
sequence again to become a WHITE DWARF.

helium star another name for a type B star in the spectral
classification, the name is used because of the strength of
the lines of neutral helium in the star's spectrum. They are
hot, blue stars with surface temperatures near 14,000K
(*see* HERTZSPRUNG-RUSSELL DIAGRAM).

Helix Nebula a NEBULA in the constellation Aquarius, and
the largest of the planetary nebula. The central star,
stripped of its outer layers, is a WHITE DWARF, a dying star.

Henry Draper Catalogue a catalogue of stars, the Draper Classification. It is a catalogue where the stars are arranged according to the characteristics of their spectrum. The basis of the work was the Harvard classification, undertaken at the beginning of the century, where the spectra of 225,000 stars, later extended to 400,000, had been recorded photographically using an objective prism (SPECTROMETER). During the work of classifying the spectra so collected, there was found to be a correlation between the type of spectrum and the colour index. As the latter was believed to be a measure of the surface temperature of the star it was considered better to change what had been a somewhat arbitrary allocation of spectral types in a strictly alphabetical order into an order directly related to the temperature as given by the COLOUR INDEX. The order which emerged, and has remained in use, is:

O B A F G K M   R N S

where O represents a hot 30,000K and therefore blue-looking star and M represents a cool, 3,000K, and therefore red-looking star, R, N and S have more complex spectra.

Another class, W for WOLF-RAYET STARS, has been added in front of O-class.

Each class is subdivided into 10, the numbers 0 to 9 being added to the class letter, thus the Sun is a G2 class star. The stars in this classification were published in the Henry Draper Catalogue; each star is identified by a number preceded by the letter HD, i.e., HD172167 which is also known as VEGA and Alpha Lyrae.

This classification is of great significance for the HERTZSPRUNG-RUSSELL DIAGRAM.

Herbig-Haro object a small NEBULA of dust and gas, it is

often associated with T TAURI stars. The high energy
radiation from the young stars illuminates the small
nebulae enabling them to be studied, it is thought that
these nebulae are contracting and may represent early
stages in star formation.

Hercules a northern sky constellation. The brightest star is
Alpha Herculis or RASALGETHI. Contained within the
CONSTELLATION are M13 or NGC6205, the brightest GLOBULAR
CLUSTER of the northern skies which contains 300,000
stars.

Hercules A a strong RADIO SOURCE associated with a large
ELLIPTICAL GALAXY. The galaxy is of type SO in the HUBBLE
CLASSIFICATION and contains a rather unusual amount of
dust; it is possible the radio emission may be caused by a
BLACK HOLE at the centre of this galaxy.

Hertzsprung gap *see* **Hertzsprung-Russell diagram**.

Hertzsprung-Russell diagram a form of graph which
highlights important characteristics of stars and also
groups them into categories. The horizontal axis
represents the surface temperature of the star, the COLOUR
INDEX (B-V) or the SPECTRAL CLASS. It starts from hot, blue,
on the left advancing to cool, red, on the right. The vertical
axis is some measure of the brightness of the star; here
absolute magnitude or luminosity with reference to the
Sun as a standard, is used. Essentially it is a colour-
brightness diagram.

  This simple idea has proved to be of great significance
for not only does it groups stars into recognizable
categories, but it also illustrates, and draws attention to,
many features which have been found to be important in
understanding the behaviour and evolution of stars. As
shown here, several different scales have been used on
the horizontal axis, this has the effect of making some

scales look rather irregular. This particular diagram has been constructed from a study of stars in the neighbourhood of the Sun; stars from other parts of the universe give diagrams which are recognizably similar but differ in detail, such differences can give valuable information. One point of interest is that the diagram shown is for stars whose distance is known so that ABSOLUTE MAGNITUDES can be found. This may not always be possible, but for a group of stars thought to belong to one CLUSTER and thus all at essentially the same distance from Earth, it is enough to use the apparent magnitude, the correction necessary to convert apparent to absolute being the same for each. Any star in the line of sight to the cluster but at a different distance would show up as inconsistent when placed on the diagram.

Three areas are well filled; the main sequence, a diagonal narrow band, above it GIANT STARS, below WHITE DWARFS. In an evolving universe they show stable situations and the main sequence, holding most stars, shows the period when each is quietly "burning" hydrogen to helium in the core, the largest fraction of the life of an active star. A star at a given position on the main sequence does not move appreciably along it; however, star masses are found to progress in order, with low masses, one tenth that of the Sun, at the lower right and smoothly to the upper left, where masses 15 or 20 times that of the Sun are found. This progression reflected the MASS-LUMINOSITY RELATION. Position along the main sequence, then, illustrates the range of stars existing at present in a steady state in their evolution.

Many stars, after exhausting the fuel in the core, expand to become giants, the evolutionary track moves upwards to the right. The HERTZSPRUNG GAP might then represent a rapid stage in evolution. As a giant, a star may have another resting phase, thought shorter and often as a variable, before evolving more or less rapidly, and sometimes spectacularly, to become a WHITE DWARF. Here, with no nucleus of fuel left, it slowly radiates away heat, cooling, becoming dim, a dying star.

It is possible from theoretical considerations to deduce the possible phases in the evolution of stars and from this the visible characteristics of the star at different states. This information can be plotted on the Hertzsprung-Russell diagram as an evolutionary track.

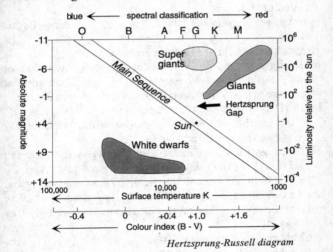

Hertzsprung-Russell diagram

highlands, lunar elevated areas on the Moon's surface, often forming mountain chains of up to 6,000m in height. They are likely to be the edges of enormous impact craters which were subsequently flooded with lava.

high velocity star a very old star travelling at a high velocity relative to the Sun (>60kms⁻¹).

Hirayama family a group of ASTEROIDS with very similar orbits. They may have originated in the break up of a larger body.

horizon an optical illusion; the line an observer apparently sees from his particular viewpoint which separates the earth, or sea, from the sky. In astronomy, the observer is supposed standing on a plane tangential to the surface of the Earth, this is the observer's horizontal plane; it is extended to cut the CELESTIAL SPHERE in a GREAT CIRCLE called the horizon.

Horsehead Nebula a dark NEBULA in the constellation Orion.

Horseshoe Nebula *see* **Omega Nebula**.

hour angle as the Earth rotates through one revolution, or 360°, in one day, it is possible to use time as an angular measure, e.g., 15° is the angle turned through in one hour.

hour circle a graduated circle on the EQUATORIAL MOUNTING of an instrument, e.g., a telescope, from which RIGHT ASCENSION may be determined.

Hubble classification a method for classifying the shapes of galaxies. Elliptical galaxies are assigned to classes E0 to E7, with E0 almost spherical, E7 lens-shaped; Spiral galaxies S0 to Sc, with Sc having long arms well away from the nucleus; barred spirals SB0 to Sbc similarly (*see* GALAXY).

Hubble constant a constant found in cosmology and related to the age of the universe. By various means it is possible to step out DISTANCE MEASUREMENTS to some galaxies. The spectra of galaxies show the familiar pattern of spectral lines, but the lines are RED SHIFTED, i.e., moved to longer wavelengths; also, the more distant the galaxy, the further the spectral lines are moved to the red.suggesting that the galaxies are receding from us, and the more distant they are from us the faster they are going. A graph of speed of recession, V, against distance from us, d, a Hubble diagram, is a straight line, so $V = H\ d$ where H is a constant, the Hubble constant, and the expression is Hubble's law. Putting in best current values for V and d gives Hubble's constant as $55\,\mathrm{kms^{-1}}$ $\mathrm{Mpc^{-1}}$. There is considerable uncertainty in the value but there seems no doubt about the Hubble law.

From the value of the Hubble constant, assuming it to have remained the same, it is possible to identify when the expansion must have commenced; this works out at about $2\ 10^{10}$ years ago, the Hubble time. This figure is not inconsistent with the estimated ages of the oldest stars.

Hubble diagram *see* **Hubble constant**.

Hubble's law *see* **Hubble constant**.

Hubble time *see* **Hubble constant**.

Hubble-Sandage variable a hot SUPERGIANT VARIABLE STAR of very high luminosity. It is thought that such stars are close to the Eddington limit beyond which RADIATION PRESSURE would be below the star's outer layers. One of the most luminous stars known, S Doradus in the LARGE MEGALLANIC CLOUD, is of this type thus they are also known as S Doradus variables. They are very massive young stars and evolve rapidly, possibly becoming SUPERNOVAE.

Hubble Space telescope a telescope put into orbit round the Earth in 1990. It is a 2.4m diameter reflecting telescope for observing in the ultraviolet, visible and infrared regions of the spectrum and carries much additional apparatus. It is not restricted to observing through

ATMOSPHERIC WINDOWS so can have a much wider range of the ELECTROMAGNETIC SPECTRUM available; it is also unaffected by optical effects caused by air movements.

Hyades an OPEN CLUSTER. It consists of about 100 stars and is sufficiently close that the PROPER MOTION of individual stars can be measured. This enables a distance measurement to be made, the cluster is found to be 40 parsecs from Earth.

Hydra a constellation lying along the celestial equator. The brightest star, Alpha Hydrae of 2nd magnitude, is also known as Alphard. R Hydrae is a variable RED GIANT star fluctuating between 4th and 10th magnitude over a time of about 390 days and resembles Mira Ceti.

Hydra A a strong RADIO SOURCE associated with a large ELLIPTICAL GALAXY. The galaxy is of type S0 in the HUBBLE CLASSIFICIATION and the radio emission may be caused by a BLACK HOLE at the centre of this galaxy.

hydrogen the lightest element. It has a nucleus of one PROTON and, as a neutral atom, therefore has one electron in orbit. Isotopes with one neutron, deuterium, and two neutrons, tritium, are known; tritium is radioactive. Deuterium and tritium have different physical properties. Hydrogen has only one electron in a shell which could hold two, it is therefore a reactive element and many compounds are known, perhaps the best known being water, H_2O. Deuterium also forms a compound with oxygen known as heavy water which has played a considerable part in nuclear research.

Hydrogen is common in all parts of the universe, accounting for two thirds of all the mass, and is thought to be the primary source of energy in stars, commonly through the FUSION REACTIONS known as the CARBON CYCLE and the PROTON-PROTON CHAIN. Liquid hydrogen/liquid oxygen fuel mixtures have been used to power many of the rockets used in space exploration.

hyperbola *see* **conic section**.

Hyperion a satellite of Saturn discovered in 1848. It is a very irregularly shaped body (410 260 220km) and has a very low ALBEDO.

I

Iapetus a satellite of Saturn, discovered by Cassini in 1671. With a diameter of 1,460km it is the third largest of 18 satellites and in an orbit of 3,560 ¥ 10³km radius, by far the most distant of the larger ones. The density, 1,200kgm⁻³, is close to that of ice, suggesting that it is mainly ice with an admixture of rock. The ALBEDO is very markedly different between the leading and trailing edges, it is possible the dark leading edge is covered with a skin of carbon-based material.

Icarus an ASTEROID discovered in 1949; it is small, perhaps 1km in diameter, and seems to be spherical. It has a very eccentric orbit and with a PERIHELION distance of 0.19 astronomical units comes within the orbit of Mercury to make the closest approach to the Sun of any object in the solar system except for comets.

image a converging lens or a concave mirror accepts light rays diverging from any specific point on an object and converges them to a corresponding point on a surface, called the image plane. Moreover, for each point on the object there is only one corresponding point on the image plane, thus an image of the object is reconstructed at the image plane. Such an image is referred to as a real image since a screen placed in the image plane would show a recognizable representation of the object, even if upside down. Other configurations are possible, e.g., by changing the object position or by use of convex mirrors or diverging lenses (where a virtual image occurs). A virtual image cannot be received on a screen but can form an object for another lens or mirror system.

image intensifier any device whereby a faint received IMAGE can be made more visible or intensified. Many methods are now available.

Imbrium basin, *Mare Imbrium*, the sea of showers. The site of an enormous impact crater, at 1,200km across, the largest on the Moon. The impacting object is thought to have been over 100km in diameter; it vaporized and melted rock at and around the impact point, shattered underlying layers and threw up enormous mountain ranges in a wide perimeter, all as it dissipated its energy. The resulting low lying CRATER was flooded from below by molten rock which had a higher density than surface material, resulting in a region of higher density on the Moon's surface, a MASCON.

immersion a phase in an ECLIPSE when the eclipsed body is entering the shadow.

inclination angle of inclination, the angle between two planes.

inferior conjunction *see* **conjunction**.

inferior planet *see* **conjunction**.

inflationary universe the theoretical idea that at a very early stage immediately after the BIG BANG the EXPANDING UNIVERSE of that era suddenly inflated or experienced an accelerated expansion for a very short time. This inflation would further explain how non-uniformities in the universe, e.g., galaxies and stars, came into being in a natural manner rather than having to explain their presence by a contrived extra concept. If inflation did occur it ought to have left its mark on the MICROWAVE BACKGROUND RADIATION in the form of slight irregularities in this radiation coming from different regions of space. Such irregularities are now being found.

infrared *see* **infrared radiation**.

infrared astronomy observation of CELESTIAL OBJECTS by the INFRARED RADIATION they emit. The use of this region of the ELECTROMAGNETIC SPECTRUM is limited for Earthbound observers as ATMOSPHERIC WINDOWS are limited, and there are umerous technical difficulties. This situation is now altered by the ability to observe from above the atmosphere. One of the most successful venture was the cooperative Infrared Astronomical Satellite, IRAS, of 1983. Much infrared astronomy is concerned with radiation produced by thermal means, i.e., BLACK BODY RADIATION. Other sources, e.g., SYNCHROTRON RADIATION are also now examined. Absorption spectra are also examined for the presence of complex molecules in space.

infrared galaxy a GALAXY emitting strongly in the INFRARED. Non black-body sources, e.g., SYNCHROTRON RADIATION, can give strong infrared emission; a BLACK HOLE, believed to occupy the centre of some galaxies can be responsible for synchrotron radiation making the galaxy a strong infrared source.

infrared radiation ELECTROMAGNETIC RADIATION lying in the electromagnetic spectrum between visible light and microwaves, 750nm up to 10^5 or 10^6nm. The radiation is most often generated by hot objects (BLACK BODY radiation).

infrared sources any hot body emits INFRARED radiation similar to a BLACK BODY, hence incandescent celestial bodies, stars, galaxies, hot gas and dust clouds, can all act as infrared sources. INFRARED RADIATION can be detected from bodies which are not incandescent, e.g., Jupiter, which show the planet to be hotter than it could become from its received solar energy, indicating an internal source of energy.

infrared telescope a telescope so constructed that it may be used with INFRARED RADIATION, in particular. Only mirrors may be used as all lenses absorb in the infrared and special detectors are required. The detectors will differ according to the region of the SPECTRUM being examined; PHOTOCELLS or PHOTOMULTIPLIERS for infrared and solid state detectors for longer wavelengths.

insolation energy coming in from the Sun in the form of radiation (as watts per square metre). On Earth, the solar constant is 1.37kWm^{-2}. It varies over the year as Earth is nearer the Sun at PERIHELION than at APHELION, and it varies with latitude and season. The amount of insolation will differ for each planet as their distances from the Sun are different.

intensity loosely, the quantity or amount of something, e.g., the intensity of radiation. It is often used in relation to energy, e.g., if the intensity of the light received is doubled, it means that the number of PHOTONS received in a given time interval is doubled.

interacting galaxies in a sense, all galaxies interact in that the gravitational attraction, of each affects all others. The term is usually reserved for cases where the interactions are unusually strong and produce marked effects. One specific case is that of the CARTWHEEL GALAXY where one galaxy passed right through another. In situations like this there may be remarkable amounts of energy released; it may be that some very strong and distant sources of radiation covering much of the electromagnetic spectrum are interacting galaxies.

interference interference occurs when two or more wave motions occupy the same region of space, or cross each other, provided they have the same wavelength and keep a constant PHASE relationship, i.e., if at any instant a crest of one lies on a crest of the other then this must remain the case at all future times. It is easier to understand the effect if the waves have the same AMPLITUDE, consider the two waves A and B with the same wavelength, and amplitude, a, as in the diagram below:

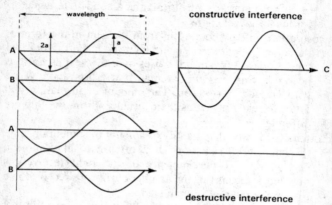

Waves A and B in the upper diagram are shown to be in phase, i.e., crests and troughs are aligned, they have the same, and a. If they are brought together into the same region of space, they interfere to give a combined effect which is of a wave of the same wavelength but twice the amplitude, 2a. This is constructive interference.

In the lower diagram the waves are out of phase, i.e., crest coincides with trough; if they are brought together into the same region of space, they interfere to give no resultant wave at all. This is destructive interference.

Note that in the diagram opposite the amplitude of the resultant wave is 2a, but the intensity is the square of the AMPLITUDE so for light waves the result would be a zone four times as bright. If the waves A and B were neither in nor out of phase but at some intermediate condition the intensity would lie somewhere between zero and $4a^2$. Clearly, if the waves did not have a constant phase relationship it would be difficult to predict the outcome. All waves can show interference effects, it is often used as a test of wave motion.

nterferometer any apparatus making use of the INTERFERENCE properties of electromagnetic waves for measurement purposes. The FABRY-PEROT interferometer enables the fine details of SPECTRAL LINES to be examined; the Michelson stellar interferometer has been used to find the diameter of stars. It is principally in radio astronomy that interferometers have found their widest application. The RESOLVING POWER of an instrument of APERTURE a and used with radiation of wavelength is given by the expression $1.22(l a)$. The wavelengths used for radio astronomy are of the order of a million times longer than the wavelengths in optical astronomy, so to get the same resolving power would require a radio telescope with a disk about a million times greater in diameter than an optical telescope, something like 2 thousand miles. Clearly this is impossible; but it is possible by using two disks, or large ARRAYS, and interferometric techniques, to produce effective apertures by aperture synthesis, of the required size. A Very Large Baseline Array is under construction using bases on the Virgin Islands and Hawaii, 5,000 miles apart.

International Atomic Time (TAI), introduced in 1972, is based on an atomic clock.

interplanetary dust *see* **interplanetary medium**.

interplanetary medium the dust and SOLAR WIND to be found in the spaces between the planets. The dust is in tiny

grains, principally in a flattened cloud surrounding th
Sun, and sunlight scattered from it causes the ZODIACA
LIGHT and its counterpart gegenschein. The dust grains ar
from 1 to 10 microns (10^{-6}m) diameter. The solar wind i
really a plasma of hot, i.e., high velocity, protons an
electrons ejected from the Sun's CORONA. At the Earth th
plasma contains only about 5 protons and electrons i
each cubic centimetre, but they are moving at velocities o
up to 400kms^{-1}; the solar wind is affected by FLARES
Interplanetary dust is replenished from METEOR STREAM
etc., but the total remains reasonably constant as dust i
deposited on planets, absorbed into the Sun etc.

interstellar extinction *see* **extinction**.

interstellar medium the contents of the space between th
stars, mainly gas and dust grains but also COSMIC RAYS an
magnetic fields as well as the whole gamut o
electromagnetic radiation. The gas is principall
hydrogen, in various degrees of dissociation, with
relatively small amount of other atomic species. Othe
hydrogen in gas clouds close to stars can become heate
or IONIZED; when mixed with dust, it gives rise to th
various forms of NEBULAE. The dust is in the form of an
small grains, perhaps 0.1 micron (10^{-7}m) diameter. It i
composed of silicates, carbon and other fragments, ofte
with icy surfaces. The material seems to come from th
STELLAR WIND and SUPERNOVA explosions. As well a
causing direct obscuring of the light from stars behind i
dust and dust clouds cause reddening of the light from
stars which does pass through (DIFFRACTION), an effec
which has to be allowed for in trying to assign a star to it
stellar classification. The dust and gas is material from
which new stars can form by gravitating into massiv
clouds which condense into STARS. Roughly one tenth o

the mass of the galaxy is in the form of gas and dust. dust and gas clouds are also found in the space between galaxies.

interstellar reddening *see* **interstellar medium**.

inverse square law for light from a small source the intensity decreases inversely as the square of the distance from the source; thus if the distance from the source is doubled, the intensity becomes one quarter. In mathematical terms, if the intensity is I, at distance d, and I_2 at d_2 then $\frac{I_2}{I_1} = \frac{d_1^2}{d_2^2}$. This relationship is used to obtain the ABSOLUTE MAGNITUDE of a star when its APPARENT MAGNITUDE and distance are known. Although expressed above for light, the relationship is quite general. GRAVITATION also follows an inverse square law; as does the force between charges.

Io a satellite of Jupiter discovered by Galileo in 1610. The diameter is 3,630km and the DENSITY 3,570kgm^{-3} are very similar to the Moon, but Io is a very lively body having many active volcanoes with plumes reaching 300km and other volcanic processes constantly changing superficial features. Much of the surface is coloured by vivid sulphur compounds, even pools of molten sulphur may be present; the thin atmosphere appears to be mainly sulphur dioxide. The energy for all this turmoil comes from gravitation forces causing tidal agitation in Io's interior; heating and melting the rocks, powering volcanic eruptions and lava flows. The orbit is nearly circular of radius about 420,000km and Io, GANYMEDE and EUROPA are locked together in orbital resonances which provide the tidal energy.

ion an atom having lost or gained one or more electrons in its outer shell; if electrons are lost it is a positive ion, if they are gained, a negative ion. Almost any form of energy can be used to form positive ions, light, RADIOACTIVITY, heat. An ion can regain an electron and the resulting change in energy is radiated as a QUANTUM of ELECTROMAGNETIC ENERGY, i.e., of a specific FREQUENCY and hence WAVELENGTH; a SPECTRAL LINE.

The ionization of atoms by heat plays an important part in the understanding of processes in, and at the surface of, stars. In stellar interiors the temperatures and other conditions are such that atoms will have been stripped of all their electrons resulting in a gas of nuclei and electrons.

ionization the process of forming IONS.

ionized layers regions in the Earth's atmosphere where IONS are formed by the action of solar radiation—the ionosphere. Such layers affect the passage of ELECTROMAGNETIC WAVES through them in different ways, for instance radio waves of short wavelength may not be affected whilst longer waves are reflected. Different layers are formed under different conditions, some are persistent, others fade rapidly at dusk. Many have been given names after their investigators, e.g. the Appleton layer, the Heaviside layer etc.

ionosphere *see* **ionized layers**.

iron meteorite a METEORITE with an unusually high iron content, only about 7% of all meteorites fall into this class.

isotope any atom of a given chemical element will always have the same number of PROTONS in its NUCLEUS and ELECTRONS in its outer shell, for it is the number of electrons which set its chemical properties. There is (usually) a second component of the nucleus, however, a neutral particle called a NEUTRON which plays no part in chemical reactions but does in nuclear reactions. The number of neutrons in a given nucleus can vary, usually one particular number predominates, but others are possible; these are called its isotopes. For instance, helium normally has two protons and two neutrons, but an isotope, known as helium three, also exists with only one neutron. Quite often isotopes are unstable and radioactivity results.

J

jansky the unit used for the measurement of the power received on Earth from a celestial RADIO SOURCE, the name commemorates Karl Jansky, a pioneer in the field.

Janus a small, irregular satellite of Saturn, in the same orbit as EPIMETHEUS.

jet a narrow stream of moving matter. Jets are found in observations of RADIO SOURCES and QUASARS. The origin is thought to be in a galaxy, probably elliptical, with a BLACK HOLE at its centre. This sucks in matter from its surroundings, the accelerated stream of matter is heated and ionized by collisions. Some of the rapidly moving charged particles are caught by magnetic fields and ejected as a jet of PLASMA. The energy given off by these processes is many times the visible light emitted from the whole galaxy. Other jets occur in astronomy; for instance the head of a COMET under the Sun's radiation evaporates, often in the form of jets. Movements of gas on the Sun's surface are known as jets.

Jewel Box cluster an open STAR CLUSTER situated close to the Southern Cross, CRUX, galaxy. The name was given by Herschel as the cluster contains many bright coloured stars including a RED GIANT Kappa Crucis.

Jovian planets the four outer planets which are similar to JUPITER, also called Jove. The innermost planets Mercury, Venus, Earth and Mars are known as terrestrial planets as they resemble the Earth but Pluto is no included; it is thought it might originally have been a satellite.

The Jovian planets are Jupiter, Saturn, Uranus, and Neptune; each is large, ranging from 48,000km diameter for Neptune to 142,000km diameter for Jupiter and has a rock-iron CORE surrounded by a mass of gaseous material. The masses range from about 14 times the Earth for Uranus to 318 times for Jupiter, the DENSITIES are therefore low, from $0.7 kgm^{-3}$ to 1.76 for Neptune. They are similar also in that each has many satellites, 18 for Saturn to 8 for Neptune; all also have a ring system, though that for Saturn is by far the most developed.

Julian calendar the CALENDAR as reformed by Julius Caesar in 46 BC.

Juliet a small satellite of Uranus. It has a diameter of about 80km and is in an orbit which is almost circular with a radius of 64 ¥ 10^3km.

Jupiter the largest and heaviest planet in the solar system. With a diameter of 142,800km and a mass of 1.9 10^{27}kg, Jupiter is by far the biggest planet, in fact it would only need to be ten times heavier to be able to initiate FUSION REACTIONS at its core to become a star. It is sometimes referred to as a BROWN STAR, the implication being that it has failed to ignite. Like all the JOVIAN PLANETS it radiates more energy than it receives from the Sun, so it must have an internal energy source.

Jupiter has an inner rocky core, perhaps ten or twenty times the mass of the Earth. Surrounding this is a liquid layer of light elements and an outer envelope in the form of a huge atmosphere. The atmosphere is in steady movement, driven largely by the planet's heat source. The motion takes the form of parallel bands moving with respect to each other and having different colours. At the boundaries between the bands small whirlpools or vortices form, one of these being the well-known and long-persisting GREAT RED SPOT. It is a kind of enormous storm in Jupiter's atmosphere, bigger than the whole Earth, and drives clouds up to very high levels. It seems to be an anticyclone, i.e., a high pressure region, thus the gas flow is from deeper levels up the centre; the red colour would appear to be from phosphorus. There is a magnetic field, much stronger than Earth's, and this leads to belts of trapped radiation equivalent to the VAN ALLEN BELTS. There is a very tenuous ring system composed of very small particles. Jupiter has a fleet of satellites, 18 in all. Four of these, known as the GALILEAN SATELLITES, were first seen by Galileo in 1610, these are Io, Europa, Ganymede and Callisto, three of which have orbits locked into resonance with each other. The other satellites divide themselves into 3 groups; the innermost, Metis, Adrastea, Amalthea and Thebe are quite small and with a tendency to be irregular and in orbits of small radius. Just beyond the Galilean satellites is another group of four, mainly small and in close orbits. Finally another group of four in close orbits, all small. The eight outer satellites have very inclined and eccentric orbits, the outer four are in retrograde motion, i.e., they move in the opposite direction in their orbits. Jupiter is a radio source.

K

K-corona the innermost region of the Sun's CORONA. It is a region where free electrons scatter light from the PHOTOSPHERE, giving the white HALO seen during solar ECLIPSES. It extends out to two or three solar radii before being overtaken by the F-corona.

kelvin the unit of measurement on the absolute or Kelvin temperature scale. The size of the degree is the same as on the Celsius scale.

Kelvin-Helmholtz contraction the concept that a mass of gas would contract under its own gravity, the energy released would be transformed into heat and this would form the source of energy for a star. The idea was mooted before NUCLEAR FUSION was understood and was the only known possible source. On this theory the life of a star would be no more than 25 million years rather than the 10 thousand million years for hydrogen "burning". It is thought, however, that the initial stages of a star's formation closely follow the contraction theory until the temperature and pressure in the core become high enough to initiate fusion.

Kelvin temperature scale the thermodynamic or absolute temperature scale which reflects that there is a minimum temperature below which it is not possible to go. Once all available energy has been removed from a body no further lowering of temperature is possible, thus there is an absolute zero of temperature. It is found to be -273.15° C and is designated 0K on the Kelvin scale. Freezing point, 0°C, becomes 273.15K and the boiling point of water 100°C, is 373.15K. At 0K atoms and molecules in gases, liquids and solids have given up all the energy possible from the various movements they have velocity, vibration and rotation.

Kepler's Laws three laws describing the motion of planets in their orbits derived from a long period of meticulous observation. The observations were carried out by Tycho Brahe and the laws derived by Johannes Kepler. The laws are:

1) every planet moves in an ellipse with the Sun at one FOCUS.

2) the radius vector, i.e., the line from the planet to the Sun, sweeps out equal areas of the orbit in equal times.

3) the periodic times, i.e., the year for each planet, are related to their average distances from the sun, the relation in (periodic time)^2 is proportional to (average distance)^3.

These laws follow from NEWTON'S LAW OF GRAVITATION. The influence of other gravitational masses and other perturbations mean that Kepler's Laws are not exact for any planet or satellite, but they remain useful.

Kepler's star otherwise known as Kepler's Nova. A SUPERNOVA explosion observed by Kepler in 1604, one of only three known to have occurred in the MILKY WAY GALAXY. The remains of the star have not been located, but a faint NEBULA with a wide range of emission in the ELECTROMAGNETIC SPECTRUM has been detected. The supernova was seen in the constellation Ophiuchus, and was said to be brighter than Jupiter.

Keyhole Nebula *see* **Carina.**

Kirkwood gaps orbits that appear to be avoided in the asteroid belt. It was shown by Kirkwood in 1867 that an

ASTEROID in any of these empty orbits would have an orbital period which would be a simple fraction of that of Jupiter. The gravitational pull of Jupiter would thus act on the asteroid for some considerable time when they were close, thus making the orbits unstable causing the asteroid to be ejected.

K star *see* **spectral classification.**

L

Lagoon Nebula M8 or NGC6523, an ionized hydrogen NEBULA in the constellation Sagittarius. A group of young, hot stars in the nebula ionize the gas which glows as the electrons return to the ions. It contains a number of small, spherical dark areas known as BOK GLOBULES; these are thought to be gas condensations which will in time lead to stars.

Lagrangian points points in the neighbourhood of two orbiting masses in which forces are balanced and in which a small mass can be in a stable position. The Trojan group of ASTEROIDS are at Lagrangian points; they travel in the same orbit as Jupiter. Jupiter and the Sun form the two orbiting bodies, and the asteroids the small mass which is stable. Geometrically the Trojan asteroids are in two positions where the Sun, Jupiter and the asteroids are the vertices of an equilateral triangle. These are the L4 and L5 Lagrangian points, the other three are situated on the line joining the Sun and Jupiter.

Large Magellanic Cloud *see* **Magellanic Clouds.**

Larissa a small satellite of Neptune. It is 190km in diameter and in an orbit 74 ¥ 10^3km radius.

last quarter a PHASE of the Moon, or other body. As seen from the Earth, the dividing line between dark and light on the Moon, the TERMINATOR, would be a straight line running over the moon's disk. It is the opposite situation to *first quarter*.

latitude on Earth, as ANGULAR MEASURE over the surface of the Earth starting from the EQUATOR and moving to either pole. It is stated in degrees, e.g., the latitude of London is about 51° 3′ North. In astronomy, the similar measurement is made on the CELESTIAL SPHERE and it is the angular distance north or south of the CELESTIAL EQUATOR; it is then called the DECLINATION.

leap year a year, about every fourth, when an extra day, 29th of February, is added. The Earth turns on its axis in 24 hours, this is the day. It also takes one year to go round the Sun in its elliptical orbit; but there is not an exact number of days in a year, it is actually about 365¼ days. Hence by adding an extra day every four years, the year and the day can be kept in step (*see* CALENDAR).

Leda the smallest satellite of Jupiter is 16km in diameter and occupies a slightly eccentric orbit considerably inclined to Jupiter's equator. The orbital radius is about 11 million kilometres.

lens a piece of transparent refracting material usually so shaped as to converge or diverge a beam of light passing through it. If the surfaces of the lens are ground to be portions of a sphere leaving the lens thicker in the centre than at the edges, then it is said to be a positive or converging or convex lens and will bring a beam of light from a very distant object to a FOCUS at one point on the axis of the lens. If the surfaces are so shaped that the lens is thinner in the centre than at the edges, it is said to be a negative, diverging or concave lens. It will then cause a beam of light passing through it to diverge, as if coming from a single point on the axis in the direction from which the light is coming which again is referred to as the focus. Many variants are possible, and seldom is a single lens used on its own.

lenticular galaxy a galaxy in the shape of a converging LENS, as if a sphere had been compressed along a diameter. In the HUBBLE CLASSIFICATION a lenticular galaxy is an ELLIPTICAL GALAXY of class E7, or a SPIRAL GALAXY of class SO.

Leo a zodiacal constellation between Virgo and Cancer. The brightest star, Alpha Leonis, is also known as Regulus and is a triple star, of the 1st magnitude. R Leonis is a variable star like Mira Ceti, it has a 310 day cycle and varies from 4th to 11th magnitude; it is a RED GIANT.

Leonids a METEOR SWARM. It occurs about once in 33 years during November. The meteor stream giving rise to the shower was the first to be identified with particles left by the passage of a COMET. It has its RADIANT in the constellation Leo.

Lepus a southern constellation with no very bright stars. Alpha Leporis is of 3rd magnitude and known as Arneb. R Leporis is a variable star like MIRA CETI with a 430 day cycle and between 6th and 12th magnitude. It is a RED GIANT, and is also known as Hind's Crimson Star.

Lexell's Comet is a lost COMET. In 1770 it came close to the Earth and its orbit indicated it should return in $5^{1}/_{2}$ years, but on its outward passage it had a close encounter with Jupiter and was never seen again.

Libra zodiacal constellation between Scorpius and Virgo with no bright stars.

libration an apparent rocking of the Moon which, over time, allows some 60% of the surface to be seen from Earth even although the Moon keeps one face turned to Earth. This rocking is produced by, in part, the fact that the Moon is in an elliptical orbit, and thus moves at different speeds as it goes round, fastest at PERIGEE and at ita slowest at APOGEE. Although it keeps the same face to Earth, what this really means is that it has a particular period of rotation about its axis. Therefore, once a month it rotates round its own axis, but once a month also it goes round its elliptical orbit at a different speed in different regions; the result is that it appears to "shake its head" slightly, thus allowing slightly more of its surface to be seen. Other effects, connected with the rotation axis direction, allow it to appear to "nod its head".

light a word which tends to be used rather non-specifically. Strictly, it is all the ELECTROMAGNETIC RADIATION in that part of the electromagnetic SPECTRUM which lies within the visible region, but it is often extended to a wide range of wavelengths which the eye cannot see, i.e., ultraviolet light and infrared light. Within the narrow definition it is confined to wavelengths between about 400nm and 750nm (blue to red). Commonly this is regarded as a range of different colours, Violet, Indigo, Blue, Green, Yellow, Orange, Red, and loosely referred to as the colours of the SPECTRUM.

Rather over half the Sun's total output of radiation falls in the visible region, and the atmosphere is relatively transparent throughout the visible spectrum. Therefore, most astronomy has been carried out using visible light, until recently, when the range has been vastly extended by raising observing instruments above the atmosphere.

The dual nature of light should always be remembered; light can be regarded both as a WAVE MOTION and also as a stream of particles, PHOTONS. Sometimes it is more useful to think of light in one way rather than the other. For instance when using INTERFEROMETERS it is the wave nature which is more applicable; when using a photoelectric cell or almost any form of camera, it is the PHOTON nature which is more appropriate.

light cone a useful way of thinking about some of the consequences of RELATIVITY. EINSTEIN showed that it was necessary to consider space and time together as a combined SPACE-TIME. He also showed that light had a finite velocity which always has the same value. In order to illustrate the combined space-time, consider one axis, often the vertical one, and let that represent time, the other axis can then represent space in some sense; if only two bodies are involved it might be enough to think of this "space" axis as being a distance, the distance between the bodies. The origin of the space-time coordinate system is taken as zero time, suppose it is the time when some event occurred and we want to see how knowledge of this event can spread, at the speed of light, into the world. Suppose we let the "event" be an atom starting to radiate light at time zero; at the velocity of light, after one second the light will have travelled 3 10^8m, 2 seconds 6 10^8m, 3 seconds 9 10^8m and so on, so we get a straight line on showing how far in distance the light can have reached in any time we choose. Now two things are important: one, the light can only have reached spaces between the sloping line and the vertical axis; two, we could make use of a perspective view to represent another dimension of space. This gives the grid-plane, illustrated opposite below, but if we rotate the sloping line of the graph opposite above around the time axis, it traces out a hollow cone, and inside this cone is all the world that the light can reach. The cone is thus filled with light from the atom moving along the time axis, it is the light cone—a region in space—time that light can reach.

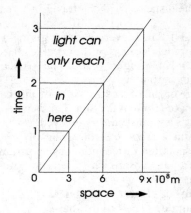

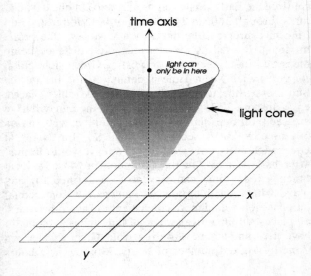

light year the distance light can travel in 1 year; there are: $365\frac{1}{2}$ 24 60 60 = 3.156 10^7 sec in a year, and light travels at 3 10^8m in every second, giving a distance of 9.467 10^{15}m in a year. Now 1 PARSEC – 3.086 10^{16}m thus 1 parsec = 3.26 light years. The parsec is usually preferred in astronomy.

limb the edge or rim of a CELESTIAL BODY that can be seen as a disk; e.g., the limb of the Sun. This is where FLARES and PROMINENCES are most easily observed.

line spectrum a SPECTRUM consisting of bright lines, an emission spectrum or a continuous spectrum crossed by dark lines, an absorption spectrum (*see* SPECTRUM, SPECTRAL LINE).

Local Group *see* **cluster of galaxies.**

local hour angle *see* **celestial sphere.**

local time the Earth rotates on its axis once in one day, i.e., turns through 360° in 24 hours. For both longitude and time measurement the GREENWICH MERIDIAN, the prime meridian, is used as the starting point; distance being measured in degrees east or west of Greenwich; Noon for Greenwich Mean Time is defined as the instant the Sun crosses the Greenwich Meridian. At outer places, e.g., Moscow, 37 35' east of Greenwich, the Sun will have crossed their meridian some time before, in fact 2 hours 30 minutes 20.12 seconds earlier. So, for Noon at Greenwich on Greenwich Mean Time, it would be just after half past two in the afternoon in Moscow local time. A local time can similarly be defined for any place where the longitude is known. For commercial purposes it is found more convenient to have time zones, all places within a given range of longitudes agreeing to have a common time differing from Greenwich Mean Time by a fixed number of hours. Moscow is 3 hours

ahead of Greenwich. SIDEREAL time is measured on the
CELESTIAL SPHERE and is similarly corrected for local
sidereal time.

Local Group of galaxies also known as Local Cluster of
galaxies. There are approximately 20 galaxies in the
neighbourhood of the MILKY WAY GALAXY, these form the
Local Group or Local Cluster. The Andromeda galaxy,
with some 3×10^{11} solar masses, is the largest, the Milky
Way has about 2×10^{11} solar masses and M33 about 10^{10}.
The nearest members are the MAGELLANIC CLOUDS, and the
group contains more elliptical forms than any other type.
The members of the Local Group are sufficiently close to
be substantially influenced by each other's gravitational
attraction.

Local Supercluster the cluster of clusters of galaxies of
which the MILKY WAY galaxy is one. It contains upwards of
50,000 galaxies all of which experience mutual
gravitational attraction. It is sometimes known as the
Virgo Supercluster.

longitude an ANGULAR MEASURE over the surface of the
Earth starting from the prime meridian, the meridian
through Greenwich, and measured in degrees east or west
round the EQUATOR. In astronomy the similar measure on
the CELESTIAL SPHERE is called RIGHT ASCENSION in the
equatorial system.

luminescence the emission of ELECTROMAGNETIC RADIATION
by a body other than as a BLACK BODY. The screen of a
television set gives off light by luminescence, the energy
coming from the beam of electrons directed towards it; a
strip-light gives off light by luminescence, the energy
coming from higher energy ultraviolet light generated in
a discharge in the tube; the light coming from an EMISSION
NEBULA, e.g., the Trifid nebula, is formed by

luminescence from gas ionized by the ultraviolet radiation from nearby very hot stars of o or b type.

luminosity the total radiation output in a given period of time from a CELESTIAL BODY, most usually a star. Most often it is compared to the Sun, thus Achernar has a luminosity of 780 times that of the Sun. It is thus a measure of brightness. The luminosity and ABSOLUTE MAGNITUDE of a star are related, and one can be found if the other is known.

lunar phases phases of the Moon. As the Moon circles the Earth, the Sun illuminates different amounts of the Moon's surface as seen from Earth. First quarter, full moon, last quarter are recognized phases corresponding to specific positions in the Moon's orbit considered relative to the Sun.

Lyman series a set of SPECTRAL LINES of specific wavelengths absorbed or given off by hydrogen gas when excited, it lies in the ultraviolet. In the quantum theory of the atom, it is shown that electrons can be stable only in particular orbits round the nucleus. An electron will normally be in the state of lowest energy, so it is normally in the orbit closest to the nucleus. Energy supplied to the electron by any means may raise it to one of the higher energy orbits, i.e., further from the nucleus. From there it will subsequently return to lower energy orbits either in one "jump" or by a series of steps from orbit to orbit. Each step, called a transition, liberates a specific quantity of energy, the difference in energy between the orbits, as a quantum of radiation having a specific frequency and thus wavelength. A series occurs when an electron makes a set of transitions from all higher energy orbits to one particular lower one. In an electric discharge lamp filled with hydrogen gas all the different allowed transitions forming a series will be present as different hydrogen atoms relax from higher excited states to lower ones. The Lyman series arises when electrons drop from all higher levels to the lowest, or ground state, level.

Lyot inventor of the coronagraph, an instrument for producing an artificial ECLIPSE of the Sun, enabling study of the CORONA.

Lyra a northern sky constellation. The brightest star, of 1st magnitude, Alpha Lyrae is also known as Vega. Beta Lyrae is a BINARY STAR, one of whose components is the prototype for Beta Lyrae stars. RR Lyrae is the prototype for an important class of VARIABLE star. The RING NEBULA and the GLOBULAR CLUSTER M56 are found in the constellation.

Lyrids a METEOR SHOWER which appears to radiate from a point in the constellation Lyra. Although not a spectacular display, it was first recorded by Chinese astronomers in 687 BC.

Lysithea a small 36km diameter, satellite of Jupiter. It is in an orbit of similar dimensions to three other satellites; quite eccentric, with a radius of about 12,000km and inclined at 29° to Jupiter's equator.

M

M a short-hand way of referring to a CELESTIAL OBJECT listed in the MESSIER CATALOGUE of 1774. It listed indistinct objects which confused him in his search for COMETS. The numbers he assigned are still in common use, often alongside the numbers in the New General Catalogue, 1888, by Dreyer referred to as NGC. For instance, the CRAB NEBULA is M1 and NGC1952.

Magellanic Clouds close neighbouring galaxies to the MILKY WAY GALAXY. The Large Magellanic Cloud or Nubecula Major is at a distance of 50,000 PARSECS, has a mass of about 10^{10} solar masses, and may be somewhat in the form of a barred spiral galaxy, one of the SB types in the HUBBLE CLASSIFICATION. The Small Magellanic Cloud, Nubecula Minor, is rather farther away at 57,000 PARSECS and smaller, having a mass of perhaps 10^9 solar masses. Its structure is less well defined and it has fewer clusters and nebulae. Part of the smaller Cloud extends towards the larger Cloud, perhaps due to gravitational forces, and gravity keeps them in orbit around the Milky Way. Both Clouds appear less developed than the Milky Way galaxy; there are fewer heavy elements present, these are thought to be produced in particularly massive stars which have evolved through SUPERNOVA explosions and scattered their outer layers into the surroundings. One blue supergiant in the Large Cloud became a supernova in 1987. Both contain stars which in general are younger than those in the Milky Way, and there is more dust and gas present. It appears that both galaxies share a common envelope of hydrogen, the *Magellanic Stream*, which may extend into the Milky Way. It was in the Small Magellanic Cloud that the important properties of CEPHEID VARIABLES were studied.

Magellanic Stream *see* **Magellanic Clouds**.

magnetic field a region of space in which magnetic effects can be detected; the region round a permanent magnet or a current carrying wire in which other magnets or current carrying wires experience forces. Magnetic fields are caused by a flow of charge, e.g., an electric current in a wire or a movement of charged particles. A permanent magnet is caused by the spin of electrons. A flow of charge entering a magnetic field experiences a force, the direction of the force being perpendicular to the direction of the field and to the direction of motion of the particle.

magnetic stars strictly speaking, all stars have magnetic fields associated with them and are thus magnetic stars; in some, however, the field is sufficiently strong to produce very significant effects and these are classified, in the Babcock Catalogue, as magnetic stars. Any charge particle in motion is affected by a magnetic field; electrons in orbit round the nucleus of an atom are therefore affected. When an electron in an atom drops from a higher energy orbit to a lower one, it radiates the energy difference as a QUANTUM of radiation, a PHOTON, and gives rise to a specific wavelength of light. If the emitting atom is in a magnetic field the wavelength is slightly charged, thus examination of the LINE SPECTRUM emitted under very high RESOLUTION, e.g., with a FABRY-PEROT INTERFEROMETER, shows the lines split in characteristic ways, with a splitting determined by the magnetic field strength. This spectral line splitting is called the ZEEMAN EFFECT. Thus the magnetic fields in stars can be found and it is observed that some VARIABLE STARS also show magnetic variations. It is thought that radiation from PULSARS is strongly affected by magnetic fields.

magnetograph a graph showing the magnetic field over the Sun. In the ZEEMAN EFFECT, a SPECTRAL LINE is split by a MAGNETIC FIELD (*see* MAGNETIC STARS), thus the wavelength of a particular line will contain split components at slightly different wavelengths. By scanning the surface of the Sun through filters set to some of these shifted wavelengths, it is possible to map out the magnetic field, getting its strength and direction.

magnetosphere *see* **geomagnetic field**.

magnitude a measure of the brightness of a star; *absolute* magnitude is an important concept in astronomy for it permits the comparison of the brightness of stars to be made directly, the absolute magnitude is defined as the brightness it would appear to have at a specific distance of 10 PARSECS; *apparent* magnitude is the brightness of a star as it is seen from Earth. If the distance to a star can be determined then the absolute magnitude can be obtained from the apparent magnitude by using the INVERSE SQUARE LAW for light.

The system of specifying the brightness of a celestial object by magnitudes is very ancient, but was reformed in 1850 by Pogson. One division of magnitude is defined as a brightness ratio of 2.512 times, e.g., a star of magnitude 5 is 2.512 times as bright as one of magnitude 6. This curious number came about by trying to preserve the brightnesses as measured in ancient records and specifically because it meant that a difference of five magnitudes gave a brightness ratio of 100 to 1, i.e., a 2nd magnitude star is 100 times as bright as a 7th magnitude one. One curious result of this reforming of the magnitude scale was that some of the brighter stars would not fit; in fact it was necessary to say some were of zero magnitude meaning they were brighter than 1st magnitudes, and indeed, to go beyond even that into negative magnitudes for objects that are brighter still. In general, stars are visible without the aid of a telescope from the brightest, i.e., zero or negative magnitude, down to the 6th magnitude. Initially magnitudes were assigned to stars by visual observation and comparing the brightness with that of a recognized standard group of stars near the north pole of the CELESTIAL SPHERE. It is now possible to measure the magnitude exactly by electronic means and the range between one magnitude and the next has been subdivided into 6. With large telescopes of great light gathering power, the faintest stars that can be seen are now beyond the 25th magnitude. Since a ratio of brightness is represented by a difference in magnitudes the scale is basically a logarithmic one. Magnitude can be related to LUMINOSITY by a mathematical formula.

main sequence a region on the HERTZSPRUNG-RUSSELL DIAGRAM representing the longest period in a star's life. It also gives an indication of the masses and colours that stars may have.

main sequence star a star occupying a place on the MAIN SEQUENCE of the HERTZSPRUNG-RUSSELL DIAGRAM.

major axis in an ellipse the line joining the two FOCI and extended to reach the ellipse.

major planet any of the larger bodies orbiting the Sun in the solar system. Mercury, Venus, Earth, Mars, Jupiter, Saturn, Uranus, Neptune and Pluto. Smaller bodies such as ASTEROIDS are excluded. Major planets are to be distinguished from the GIANT PLANETS, Jupiter, Saturn, Uranus and Neptune.

manganese star an unusual star with a SPECTRUM showing a remarkable excess of manganese, with gallium, yttrium and often mercury. It is one of the forms taken by peculiar A-type stars; the origin of these abundance anomalies is not known.

mare a large impact crater on the Moon's surface which was later filled with lava. Most events causing maria are thought to have happened between three and four thousand million years ago. They are all on the side of the moon which faces the Earth and appear dark because the lava-borne rock has a different constitution from the crust around it with a lower ALBEDO. Maria tend to have raised, mountainous, rims.

Markarian galaxy a galaxy which emits particularly strongly in the ultraviolet. Usually the emission is from the nucleus, occasionally from a more extended region. Where the source is localized in the nucleus, three types are recognized, SEYFERT galaxies, N-type galaxies and QUASARS. Those where the source is not localized resemble galaxies where recent star-formation has occurred.

Mars the fourth planet out from the Sun and next to Earth, it is the outermost of the terrestrial planet. Mars is in an elliptical orbit of average radius 1.52 ASTRONOMICAL UNITS, taking about 687 Earth days to complete. It spins on an axis inclined at about 25° to the orbital plane, similar to Earth's 23½°, taking only a very little longer, 24.6 earth hours, for one revolution. Mars has a diameter of 6,787km, about half that of earth with a mass only one tenth that of Earth and a DENSITY of 3.94 ¥ 10^3kgm^{-3}. This last figure is the lowest of the terrestrial planets. Accordingly surface gravity is low, one third of the

Earth's, and so is the ESCAPE VELOCITY. The low density suggests a less compacted body with probably no liquid core; the magnetic field is very weak. There are two very small satellites, Phobos and Deimos.

In spite of the low escape velocity an atmosphere exists, but surface pressure is only 1% of that on Earth and it is mainly carbon dioxide with but little nitrogen. There are two polar caps, very thin surface features of snow, ice and solid carbon dioxide, which change with the seasons. The mean surface temperature is near -23ºC, equatorial temperatures vary from 10ºC by day to -75ºC at night, reflecting the poor heat retaining properties of the thin atmosphere. However, clouds are frequent and dust storms often blow over considerable areas, changing the superficial appearance. The surface is solid, predominantly red in colour from the type of rock, and with very variable characteristics; areas are covered with many impact craters, similar to the Moon and Mercury, but there are also huge lava plains, mainly in equatorial regions, perhaps covering earlier crater formations. The lava came from volcanic activity, now extinct; one particular source, the volcano Olympus Mons, has a height of 23km, the largest of the solar system. As well as elevated plains there are deep valleys, one a major feature of the equatorial region, and others are found more often in the northern hemisphere. Some features are almost certainly the result of running water, although none is now found. The dust storms create a flowing pattern of sand dunes which are frequently moved. The ALBEDO is low, but the characteristic red colour and the occasional near approach of Earth and Mars can make it a dominant feature of the night sky which has exerted a fascination from ancient times.

mascon a local concentration of mass at the lunar surface associated with the MARIA.

maser *m*icrowave *a*mplification by *s*timulated *e*mission of *r*adiation; spontaneous radio emission from a few excited molecules in a gas cloud triggers surrounding excited molecules into stimulated emission of the same energy, frequency and wavelength thus a concentrated wave of emission travels through the gas gathering energy as it travels, creating intense spectral lines. These give RADIO SOURCES which can be detected at great distances. The similar process occurring at shorter, optical, wavelengths is known as a laser.

mass the quantity of matter in a body. Two phenomena are particularly associated with mass; (i) inertial mass which is the quantity found when, *a*, the acceleration of a body, is measured as a function of the force, *F*, acting on it. This is expressed in Newton's second law of motion $F = ma$, the constant of proportionality, *m*, is the inertial mass. (ii) gravitational mass, which is the mass as expressed in Newton's law of universal GRAVITATION, the force, *F*, between two bodies of masses m_1 and m_2 a distance *r* apart is given by $F = G, \frac{m_1 m^2}{r^2}$ where G is a FUNDAMENTAL CONSTANT. The equivalence of inertial mass and gravitational mass has been verified to great accuracy. In the theory of RELATIVITY, inertial mass is shown to vary with velocity especially at velocities close to that of light.

mass defect in NUCLEAR FUSION and NUCLEAR FISSION reactions it is found that the total mass of the reacting nuclei is greater than the total mass of the nuclei produced; this difference is known as the mass defect.

mass-luminosity relation; an observed relationship between the mass of a star and its LUMINOSITY. It is found that the luminosity, L, is related to its mass, M, by the expression, $L = AM^k$ where A and k are constants, k having the value of about 3.1. It is usually shown by plotting a graph of luminosity, which is a logarithmic measure of radiation output, against the logarithm of the mass. Over much of the range it is a straight line, but falls away at both ends, for very light, dim stars and very heavy, bright stars, i.e. white dwarfs and red giants. A central straight line portion corresponds to MAIN SEQUENCE STARS of the HERTZSPRUNG-RUSSELL DIAGRAM.

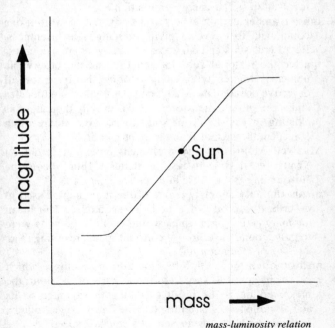

mass-luminosity relation

The relationship is useful for finding either the mass or the luminosity of a star if the other quantity is known. For instance, a distant BINARY STAR may, in favourable circumstances, have a known mass, The absolute magnitude would then follow from the mass-luminosity relation and the apparent magnitude is easily measured. Comparison between the absolute and apparent magnitudes allows the distance of the star to be found from the inverse square law. The relationship has also proved important in understanding the mechanisms involved in stellar energy production.

mass transfer certain BINARY STARS transfer mass from one component to the other giving variations in brightness. Beta Lyrae stars and CATACLYSMIC VARIABLES are examples.

matter the material substance that forms the observable universe. Matter with energy forms the basis of all objective phenomena. Matter consists of atoms, molecules and some sub-atomic particles and is usually thought of as existing in gas, liquid or solid form. PLASMAS are often considered to be a different state of matter.

Maxwell Montes a very prominent mountain found on Venus by radar surveys, it stands 11km above the surrounding Ishtar Terra highlands.

mean anomaly anomaly is one of the three angles used to describe the orbit of a body in an ellipse. The mean anomaly is the angle which would result if the body were to move round the ellipse at constant speed, resulting in an average or mean motion.

mean motion the Earth orbits the Sun in an ellipse which causes its speed to vary in different parts of the orbit; the mean motion is the result of taking the average of its actual motion, i.e., assuming that the Earth moved round a fictitious body, the mean Sun, at a constant speed.

mean solar day *see* **equation of time**.

mean solar time *see* **mean motion, equation of time**.

Merak Beta Ursae Majoris, a 2nd magnitude star in the constellation Ursa Major or the Great Bear. Dubhe, also in the constellation, and Merak form a POINTER from which the POLE STAR can be located.

Mercury the innermost, and apart from Pluto, the smallest planet in the solar system; a terrestrial planet. It is in a markedly elliptical orbit of approximate radius 0.39 ASTRONOMICAL UNITS, inclined at 7 to the ECLIPTIC, a greater inclination than all the others except for Pluto. Mercury takes about 88 earth days to complete one orbit and it rotates slowly on its axis, taking about 58 earth days for one revolution. Thus Mercury's day is nearly two thirds of its year. Mercury has a diameter of 4,878km, 38% of Earth's diameter, and a mass only 6% of Earth's; this gives an average DENSITY of $5.43 kgm^{-3}$, very close to Earth's density. Surface gravity is low and very similar to that of Mars, about one third of that on EARTH; the ESCAPE VELOCITY is correspondingly low. Mercury is the only planet not to have a satellite.

Because of the low escape velocity only the most tenuous of atmospheres exists; it does nothing to lessen surface temperature extremes. With its nearness to the Sun and its elliptical orbit the equatorial surface temperature, during the long day, varies from 285C when farthest from the Sun to 415ºC when closest, but falls to −175ºC at night. The surface is covered with impact craters similar to those on the Moon, the largest feature is known as Caloris Basin, 1,300km in diameter.

Irregularities in the orbit have been explained by, and test the correctness of, the theory of RELATIVITY.

meridian *see* **celestial sphere, longitude, latitude**.

Messier Catalogue celestial objects other than stars are usually referred to by their M number, the number assigned in Messier's Catalogue.

Me stars *see* **star classification**.

meteor a 'shooting star', the streak of light seen on a clear night when a METEOROID burns itself out because of friction in its passage through the Earth's upper atmosphere. This usually happens at heights of about 75 to 115km. If the meteoroid is not very small its passage through the atmosphere slows, and it ends up as a dust grain. A few larger meteoroids fall direct to earth; they are known as meteorites. The visible glowing tail contains ionized atoms and molecules, they reflect RADAR thus meteors can be observed in daylight. A visible meteor is typically caused by a meteoroid of about a centimetre diameter with a weight of about 0.1 gram. Sporadic meteors are those not associated with METEOR SHOWERS.

meteorite a METEOROID which has passed through the Earth's atmosphere as a meteor to land on the surface. A meteoroid requires to have a mass of several grams and to encounter the Earth's atmosphere at low velocity, most of the mass is burned off in passage through the atmosphere. About six meteorites are recovered in a year. They are fragments of asteroids with eccentric orbits which cross the Earth's orbit.

meteoroid a small body that on entering the Earth's atmosphere is heated by friction and leaves a bright trail, a METEOR. If it is massive enough some of it may reach the Earth's surface as a METEORITE. Most meteoroids are dust particles or debris from COMETS, with masses ranging from thousands of kilograms to micrograms. They are often seen in groups, known as a METEOR SHOWER and arise from a METEOR STREAM, the debris left in the orbit of a comet.

meteor shower a group of METEORS that appear to come
from one point on the CELESTIAL SPHERE. Each shower is
named after the constellation in which this radiating point,
or RADIANT, is situated. The shower has its origin in a
METEOR STREAM, the debris left by a comet in its path, when
the Earth moves through it. Examples are the AQUARIDS,
radiant in AQUARIUS; the LEONIDS, radiant in LEO, and the
ORIONIDS, radiant in ORION. Since the paths of comets are
narrow and in a defined position a given distance from the
Sun, if the Earth once cuts across the orbit of a comet, it
will do so again once a year, thus allowing dates to be
given when a shower would be expected.

meteor stream *see* **meteoroid, meteor shower**.

Metis the innermost satellite of Jupiter. It is very small,
40km diameter, and has very nearly the same orbit as
Adrastea

Michelson interferometer a devise using the interference
of light to make very accurate measurements of lengths. A
beam of monochromatic, i.e., single wavelength, light is
split into two beams by a partially reflecting mirror. The
two beams are sent by separate paths and subsequently
reunited, interference occurs when they are recombined
and the form of interference depends on any
dissimilarities in the one path as compared to the other.
The apparatus has been used to measure the length of the
standard metre in terms of the wavelength of light, and a
similar apparatus was used in the Michelson - Morley
experiment intended to show any anisotropy in the
velocity of light.

Michelson stellar interferometer *see* **interferometer**.

microdensitometer a device for determining in a
quantitative manner the density, or degree of blackening,
of a photographic plate. This is used to convert the image

of a star into a measurement of the brightness of the star and ultimately to a determination of its APPARENT MAGNITUDE. The device consists of a light source focused to a fine beam which is passed through the developed image on the photographic plate before falling on a PHOTOCELL. The photocell converts the intensity of the received light into a current, so as the light spot is moved across the photographic plate, the variations in darkness are converted to variations in electric current. The device can also be used for analysing a spectrum recorded on a photographic plate, e.g., investigating the structure of SPECTRAL LINES, line profiles.

micrometeorite a very small meteoritic particle that loses its energy before burning up in the Earth's atmosphere and than falls to the surface as dust.

microwave background radiation *see* **big bang theory**.

Milky Way Galaxy *see* **galaxy**.

Mimas a satellite of Saturn, found by Herschel in 1789. It is about 392km in diameter and is probably mainly water-ice. The surface is heavily cratered, with one giant crater, named Herschel, roughly a third of the size of the whole body.

minute used in two senses; in time it isone sixtieth of an hour; in ANGLULAR MEASURE it is one sixtieth of a degree; in both cases it is subdivided into 60 seconds.

Mir the name given to the Russian space station, continuously manned since 1986.

Mira also known as Mira Ceti; Omicron Ceti, a BINARY STAR in the constellation Cetus, which lies across the CELESTIAL EQUATOR. Mira was the first known regular VARIABLE. It is the prototype for a class of variable star, the Mira variables. The brighter component is a RED GIANT whose magnitude varies from 3.5 to 9.1 with a 322 day period. It

is a pulsating star with a mechanism similar to that of
CEPHEID VARIABLES, but with hydrogen rather than helium
as the ionizing and recombining gas.

Miranda a satellite of Uranus, discovered in 1948. It has a
diameter of 480km and is in a near-circular orbit of radius
$129\ 10\ ^3$km. The surface appears to consist of two or three
distinct regions; an old, very heavily cratered area, and a
newly formed very complex area almost without craters,
but with slopes, ridges and valleys probably of volcanic
origin. One theory is that Miranda was broken apart into
pieces, perhaps by a collision, the pieces subsequently
reforming.

mirror a highly polished, regular surface, coated with a
material to reflect light strongly. The essential feature is
that any imperfections are small compared to the
wavelength of the light used, so that the surface will
reflect the light rather than diffusely scatter it. In
astronomy, mirrors are used in telescopes in preference to
lenses for many reasons amongst which are; it is easier to
form the one surface of a mirror into the required shape
rather than the two surfaces of a lens and also allow for
any variations in refractive index of the glass; a reflecting
mirror can be supported over the entire face, a
transmitting lens only round the rim, this becomes
significant for big mirrors or lenses of very many tons
weight; a mirror, unlike a lens, does not suffer from
CHROMATIC ABERRATION; a mirror does not absorb light, the
thickness of a lens ensures considerable absorption. Most
telescope mirrors are ground to be a portion of a sphere,
and then coated with a thin, uniform layer of aluminium,
usually by vacuum deposition. The coating can be
reformed should the need arise.

Mizar Zeta Ursae Majoris, a 2nd magnitude MULTIPLE STAR in the constellation Ursa Major. Two components are hot DWARF STARS moving in an orbit with a very long period; this was the first double star to be found, in 1650. The brighter star is also a SPECTROSCOPIC BINARY, again the first to be found, in 1889; and the fainter star is another spectroscopic binary. The distant Alcor, of 4th magnitude completes the system.

MK system also known as MKK system; a star classification system based on spectral type and luminosity. It is similar to the Harvard classification, used in the HENRY DRAPER CATALOGUE, and like it, forms the basis of the HERTZSPRUNG-RUSSELL DIAGRAM.

molecule one of the groups of atoms in which material substances normally exist. For instance, hydrogen gas normally consists of two hydrogen atoms bound together as a molecule, written H_2, oxygen shows the same characteristics O_2; on the other hand, helium gas consists of single atoms of helium. More complex molecules, essentially compounds, also occur, e.g., water vapour consists of two atoms of hydrogen chemically bound to one atom of oxygen, H_2O, the whole forming one molecule. Certain molecules are very stable and can be found even in stellar spectra.

Monoceros a constellation running across the CELESTIAL EQUATOR. It is faint, brightest star is 4th magnitude, but lies in the Milky Way and contains many interesting CELESTIAL OBJECTS. One of these is the Rosette Nebula; it consists of a shell of gas, an emission NEBULA, glowing in the light from two stars of a GLOBULAR CLUSTER within it. In the nebula are small, round dark areas BOK GLOBULES which may be future stars condensing under gravity from the cloud of dust and gas. Another feature is the star cluster NGC2264 containing a huge very luminous SUPERGIANT, S

Monocerotis. Also present is Plaskett's star, a 6th magnitude spectroscopic binary whose component stars are each at least 55 times the mass of the sun, the most massive binary star known.

month a period of time determined by the time the Moon takes to complete one orbit of the Earth.

Moon the only natural satellite of the Earth. It is in a near circular orbit of mean radius 384,000km inclined at just over 5 to the ECLIPTIC; as seen from Earth, the synodic month averages 29.53 days. The same face is always kept toward Earth, so the Moon's period of spin on its axis is the same as its period of revolution round its orbit. Small oscillations, LIBRATIONS, allow 59% of the surface to be seen from Earth over a period. The orbit is perturbed by gravitation effects from the Sun and also planets, these influences combine to give cyclical changes known as inequalities.

The Moon's diameter is 3,476km, roughly one quarter that of Earth, but its mass is only 1.2% of the Earth's, resulting in a mean DENSITY of 3.34kgm^{-3}. This is very close to that of the rocks at, and just beneath, the Earth's surface. The surface gravity is low, one sixth of Earth's, and as the ESCAPE VELOCITY is correspondingly small, there is virtually no atmosphere. With no blanketing effect, the surface temperature is subject to a wide range, +100ºC in full sun, −200ºC at night. This temperature cycle causes a slow crumbling of the rock.

The surface is very heavily cratered, almost certainly by impact. On the side facing the Earth are very old, very large craters called MARIA; up to 1,000km in diameter, they have been filled with darker lava from below the surface (*see* IMBRIAN BASIN). This produces a solidified rock more massive than its surroundings, the maria are therefore the site of MASCONS. From many of the craters bright rays are seen to cover great lengths across the surface; this is probably due to material ejected form the site of impact. The side of the Moon never seen from Earth is similarly cratered, but differs in that it has no maria. This is interpreted to mean that the crust is thicker there. Wherever craters have been, and especially round the maria, great mountain ranges have been thrown up. Although some are named after mountains on Earth, and even have similar heights, the mode of formation was quite different. There seems to be no trace of free water ever being on the Moon. Rock samples returned by the Apollo missions have been dated to at least four thousand million years ago, similar to the time of formation of the Earth. The cratering is thought to date back to a few hundred million years after the body was formed.

morning star *see* **evening star**.

moving cluster a form of OPEN CLUSTER in which the stars are close enough to Earth for their PROPER MOTION to be determined.

M stars *see* **stellar classification**.

M-type asteroid an ASTEROID with a spectrum containing metallic lines.

muon an unstable elementary particle with a mass about 200 times that of an electron.

N

Nadir the point on the CELESTIAL SPHERE directly beneath the
observes; the opposite point to the ZENITH. More loosely,
the lowest point.

Naiad the smallest and innermost satellite of Neptune,
which is 60km diameter and has an orbit of radius 48.23 x
10^3km.

naked-eye object any celestial body which can be seen
without the use of any optical device, e.g. binoculars,
telescope etc.

n-body problem the orbital motions of a number,
unspecified but given the symbol n, of bodies under their
mutual gravitation. Such a set of bodies is formed by the
SOLAR SYSTEM, where n is 10, or can be many more if all
satellites are included. There is no possible analytical
solution to an n-body problem, but numerical solutions
can be found to a considerable degree of accuracy. It has
so far not been possible to start from the present
configuration of the solar system and calculate backwards
to find how it evolved and from what initial state; CHAOS
THEORY applies, where small effects produce large, often
unpredictable results.

nebula a dark or light hazy patch which cannot be resolved;
a cloud of INTERSTELLAR MATTER, gas mixed with dust found
frequently in GALAXIES. Dark nebulae or ABSORPTION
NEBULAE have much dust which blocks light from more
distant stars by absorbing, scattering or reflecting it.

Bright nebulae are in four recognized classes; EMISSION, REFLECTION, PLANETARY and SUPERNOVA REMNANTS. Emission nebulae glow by fluorescent light from a gas, usually hydrogen, which is ionized by intense ultraviolet radiation from a nearby O - or B - type star. Reflection nebulae are visible by the light reflected from dust grains in the gas cloud; the spectrum is principally that of neighbouring stars, but is polarized by scattering and reflection. A planetary nebula appears as a ring surrounding a very hot star, typically 50,000K, which appears dim due to its small size. The outer shells of gas ejected from this dying star form a sphere which appears as a ring since it shows up only where the greatest depth through the very tenuous cloud is found. The cloud can be shown to be expanding by observing the DOPPLER EFFECT in it's spectrum. More than 1000 are known in the MILKY WAY GALAXY, e.g. the Helix Nebula NGC7293 in Aquarius. Supernova remnants have a somewhat similar origin, but due to the much more violent explosion are more irregular, less ring shaped, and have internal filaments, e.g. the Crab nebula M1 or NGC 1952.

nebular hypothesis a theory, initially by Laplace, which sought to explain the formation of the solar system as condensations in a disk of gas whirling round as it contracted under its own gravity. Serious difficulties are encountered in attempting to explain the details of each planet's size, structure, spin and orbit, but some modification of the simple theory is thought to hold out the best hope of reaching a satisfactory model.

Neptune discovered in 1846, the eighth planet from the Sun. It is in a near circular orbit of just over 30 astronomical units (4,496 ¥ 10^6km) which it completes in about 165 Earth years. The spin axis is inclined at $29^1/_2°$, slightly more than that of Earth or mars. The planet is 17.2 times the mass of the Earth and with an equatorial diameter of 48,600km has an average density of 1.76 10^3 kgm^{-3} suggesting a largely gaseous composition, perhaps on a rock hard ice core. The surface density and thus ESCAPE VELOCITY are higher than on Earth. There is some source of internal energy, as for Jupiter and Saturn, as Neptune emits 2.7 times as much heat as it receives from the Sun. The atmosphere is most probably hydrogen, shows levels and zones as occur in the other giant planets and a localized feature known as the GREAT DARK SPOT, an atmospheric vortex is overlaid by white clouds. There are three rings and 8 known satellites. The largest is Triton which is of similar size to Earth's moon and orbits the planet in the opposite direction to Neptune's spin. It may have been captured some time after formation. Neptune was located as a result of observations of irregularities in the orbits of Uranus and, in turn, irregularities in the orbit of Neptune led to the search for and discovery of Pluto.

ereid the outermost satellite of Neptune. It is 300km in diameter, and lies in a highly eccentric orbit of considerable inclination. It has an irregular shape and an ALBEDO of 0.14.

eutrino a subatomic elementary particle whose existence was first proposed by Pauli in 1930 in order to explain characteristic features of BETA PARTICLE EMISSION from RADIOACTIVE materials. The neutrino has no charge and may have no mass when at rest, but does carry spin. Its existence has been experimentally confirmed, though it is very difficult to find due to its non-interacting nature. These are three recognized forms of neutrino.

eutrino astronomy the NEUTRINO should be a product of the NUCLEAR FUSION reactions which generate energy in the

Sun. It can be detected by a very rare reaction with an ISOTOPE of chlorine, and vast tanks of chlorine compounds shielded by being kept at the bottom of mine shafts, are used to look for evidence of neutrinos. Difficulties have arisen, because the number of neutrinos found coming from the Sun is only one third of that predicted. It has also been proposed that the problem arising in cosmology of the mass of the universe being only about one tenth that required to fit with theoretical predictions could be solved if neutrinos were plentiful and had some rest mass.

neutron a subatomic elementary particle and a component, along with the PROTON, of all atomic nuclei. It has a mass similar to that of a proton but no charge and carries spin. It is a product of, and instigator of, nuclear fission reactions. A free neutron is unstable, decaying spontaneously to a proton and an electron. It is thought that under the extreme pressures in stellar cores once nuclear fusion reactions have ceased, the atoms collapse with the outer electrons being united with the protons to form neutrons.

neutron star a star of exceptional density. In its core, after the energy release from FUSION REACTIONS has finished, gravitational collapse continues and the atoms are crushed so that the electrons are incorporated into the protons to form primarily NEUTRONS. The density rises to 10^{13} or 10 times that of water, and the diameter of the collapsed star is only 10–20km. With the low surface area this entails, even if they are very hot, the emission of energy is small and they are difficult to detect. Neutron stars are thought to be the final evolutionary stage for most stars with a mass between 1.44 (the CHANDRASEKHAR LIMIT) and 3 times the mass of the Sun. However stars above three solar masses form BLACK HOLES. Rotating magnetic neutron stars are thought to be observable as PULSARS.

Newton's Law of Gravitation *see* **gravitation.**

N galaxy also known as N-type galaxy; a galaxy with a pronounced star-like nucleus having a faint surrounding haze. N galaxies are usually strong RADIO SOURCES and may evolve into QUASARS.

N.G.C. also known as New General Catalogue; *see* **catalogue**.

noctilucent clouds a rare form of cloud, probably ice crystals and meteoric dust forming at about 82km above Earth's surface, higher than any other clouds. Only occasionally visible in midsummer nights at high altitudes as they are illuminated by light from the Sun far below the observer's horizon.

node one of two points diametrically opposite each other, in which the orbit of a celestial body, e.g. Moon or a planet, cuts the ECLIPTIC on the CELESTIAL SPHERE.

noise in electronics and information theory any random, unpredictable and undesirable signals that mask the desired information content. Noise is often a result of high temperatures, thus many detectors for light or other radiation are operated under refrigeration, e.g. surrounded by liquid nitrogen, hydrogen, or helium.

non-thermal radiation any ELECTROMAGNETIC RADIATION not generated by a hot body; most hot bodies radiate in a characteristic manner similar to that of a BLACK BODY. If the radiation does not show this spectral distribution it is classified as non-thermal radiation. For instance, an ordinary filament bulb gives off light from a hot filament and covers a wide spectrum, most emission not being in the visible range. A fluorescent lamp, however, gives off light by a two-stage process in which an electrical discharge in a gas generates ultraviolet light which in turn is used to cause a phosphor to glow by LUMINESCENCE.

noon *see* **day**.

North America Nebula a NEBULA in the constellation Cygnus which vaguely resembles the North American continent. It is largely an EMISSION NEBULA with ionized hydrogen excited by very hot, very massive stars.

northern lights *see* **aurora Borealis**.

north polar distance the angular distance of a CELESTIAL OBJECT on the CELESTIAL SPHERE measured from the north celestial pole to the object along a MERIDIAN. The DECLINATION is the ANGULAR MEASURE along the same meridian but measured from the equator up to the celestial body; the declination angle added to the north polar distance angle gives 90.

nova a CATACLYSMIC VARIABLE STAR whose LUMINOSITY suddenly increases from 10^3 to 10^5 times normal and reaches a maximum luminosity within days. After a period of brightness, the star more slowly returns to normal over a few weeks. The mechanism is thought to be based on a BINARY STAR SYSTEM in which one member is a WHITE DWARF with a very close companion. Gas is attracted from the companion onto the dwarf where it erupts as a nuclear fusion reaction, throwing off some of the gas as a shell.

nuclear fission a type of NUCLEAR REACTION in which a heavy nucleus splits into two daughter nuclei of similar masses with several NEUTRONS and other fragments released. There is an accompanying energy release as the mass of the original nucleus is greater than the sum of the masses of the products, this mass object being converted to energy as indicated in EINSTEIN'S MASS-ENERGY relationship. Nuclear fission can be spontaneous, i.e. natural, o induced; if the latter it is often used in a nuclear reactor in a controlled fashion for power generation.

nuclear fusion a type of NUCLEAR REACTION in which lighte

NUCLEI are caused to fuse together to form heavier nuclei; as the mass of the heavier nucleus is less than the sum of the masses of the fusing nuclei, there is a MASS DEFECT and energy is released as indicated by EINSTEIN'S MASS-ENERGY RELATIONSHIP. Nuclear fusion reactions, in which hydrogen is fused to form helium either directly or in a chain process, are thought to be the energy sources for stars. They can only take place under conditions of very high pressures and temperatures.

nuclear reaction any reaction in which the nuclei of atoms take direct part. Ordinary chemical reactions involve only the outer electrons, the nuclei do not play a part. RADIOACTIVE DECAY, NUCLEAR FISSION and NUCLEAR FUSION are all nuclear reactions.

nucleon either a PROTON or a NEUTRON, the ordinary components of a nucleus.

nucleosynthesis in the BIG BANG theory it is thought that matter first appeared in the form of PROTONS and NEUTRONS and for a very brief period conditions were right for FUSION REACTIONS to take place to build heavier NUCLEI. This is nucleosynthesis. The process in believed to take place in stars at present.

nucleus the name given to the central region of many things, e.g. an ATOM, a COMET, or a GALAXY.

O

Oberon the outermost and second largest satellite of Uranus, discovered by Herschel in 1787. It has a diameter of 1,524 km and lies in a near circular orbit about 584 x 10^3km in diameter, taking 13,463 Earth days to complete one orbit. The density is 1.5 x 10^3 kgm^{-3}, suggesting that it is a body formed from ice and rock. The surface is cratered, some large and with bright rays, some with dark interiors.

objective also known as the objective lens is the front lens in a refracting telescope which forms the first image of the object under examination. This image is then examined through the eyepiece. The magnifying power of a simple refracting, telescope is given by the ratio f_o/f_e where f_o is the FOCAL LENGTH of the objective lens and f_e is the focal length of the eyepiece; hence for reasonable magnification, f_o is large, giving a thin lens. Further, the light gathering power is determined by the diameter of the objective, thus the objective lens if usually a large diameter but relatively thin lens of long focal length.

objective prism a glass PRISM of small refracting angle used with a telescope to form a small SPECTRUM from all of the stars in the field of view. Typically it is an accessory to the telescope and is fixed over the OBJECTIVE lens thus transforming the telescope into a simple spectrograph. The images of all stars are then dispersed into a short spectrum with sufficient detail to make obvious the

SPECTRAL CLASSIFICATIONS of the stars in a considerable region of the sky at one time. Detailed spectral analysis is carried out on individual star images by use of a SPECTROMETER examining the light from each star of interest in turn.

oblateness the measure of the difference between the actual shape of a CELESTIAL BODY and a perfect sphere. Most celestial bodies are spinning on an axis causing the shape of the body to be distorted from that of a perfect sphere. The spin causes a bulge at the equator with a consequent flattening at the poles. The Earth has an equatorial radius of 6,378.2 km and a polar radius of 6,356.8 km, the ratio of these two figures, 1.00337 or 1/297 is taken as a measure of the oblateness. The corresponding figure for Saturn is 1/9.5.

obliquity of the ecliptic the angle between the plane of the EARTH'S EQUATOR, i.e., the plane perpendicular to its spin axis, and the PLANE of the ECLIPTIC, i.e., the plane containing its orbit. It is the same as the angle of tilt made by the Earth's spin axis, about $23^{1}/_{2}°$.

observatory any place from which astronomical observations are made. Most large observatories specialise in observations in one particular region of the ELECTROMAGNETIC SPECTRUM, e.g., using optical or radio telescopes, and most have specialised buildings designed to house their instruments. Many optical observatories are located in remote mountain-top areas where the air is thin, relatively free from pollution and uninfluenced by nearby city lights.

occultation the blocking of the light from a distant star or other CELESTIAL BODY by the movement of a nearer, solar system, object across its line of sight. Such occultations can reveal much information about both bodies involved.

For instance, details may be determined of any possible traces of atmosphere on the nearer body or the pressure of a close BINARY SYSTEM for the further body. An ECLIPSE or a TRANSIT is a form of occultation.

OH source the OH or hydroxyl radical is a MOLECULE formed from a chemical combination of an oxygen and a hydrogen atom. It is not a stable compound but has been detected in intergalactic material by spectral lines in the radio region of the ELECTROMAGNETIC SPECTRUM. OH radicals are found in comet tails.

Olbers' paradox a seemingly-innocent question asked by Olbers in 1826 (1758-1840) "Why is the sky dark at night?" The significance of the question lies in the realisation that no matter in which direction an observer looks there must be a star present in that direction. It would be very faint because of its distance but from all neighbouring points there would be light from other stars, thus covering the CELESTIAL SPHERE with sources filling every possible point of view and all having as much radiation, at least, as the Sun. Thus the night sky ought to be at least as bright as the surface of the sun. The situation envisaged by Olbers remains true today, substituting galaxies of stars for single stars, and the observed darkness must therefore have some explanation. It may lie, partially, in the presence of gas and dust clouds obscuring regions of the sky, but the main cause is the RECESSION OF THE GALAXIES produced by the EXPANSION OF THE UNIVERSE. All galaxies are on average observed to be receding from us as the universe expands, the light from a distant galaxy is thus noticeably affected by a reddening of its light, the RED SHIFT, every wavelength becoming longer, due to the DOPPLER EFFECT. For very far distant galaxies this red shift is so extreme that little of its light is visible from Earth.

Omega Centauri *see* **centaurus.**

Omega Nebula an emission nebula in the constellation Sagittarius which radiates radio wavelengths as well as visible light.

Oort Cloud otherwise known as the Öpik-Oort Cloud; a cloud of cometary nuclei thought to be in orbits at the fringes of the solar system, perhaps from the time of its origin. Their orbits are so eccentric that only when an occasional nucleus comes close to the Sun, and thus under the influence of solar radiation, does it develop a tail and the other characteristics of a comet.

Oort's constants quantities introduced by Oort in his study of the PROPER MOTIONS of stars. The stars in the MILKY WAY GALAXY, like the Sun, are in motion in some form of elliptical orbit around the centre of mass of the galaxy. As seen from Earth, this results in some of the nearer stars having considerable proper motions, i.e., moving across the CELESTIAL SPHERE, and also radial velocities, i.e., moving towards or away from Earth, this motion being revealed by the DOPPLER EFFECT on their spectra. Oort devised a simple formula to describe this motion and introduced two constants necessary to fit the observed motions of individual stars. His description of the motion follows KEPLER'S LAWS.

opacity a quantity expressing the amount of absorption or scattering of ELECTROMAGNETIC RADIATION in its passage through material, most often dust or GAS-CLOUDS or PLASMAS. Any given photon of the radiation has a free path, which is long in a low opacity medium, short in regions of high opacity, after which it makes some sort of interaction with the medium (SCATTERING or ABSORPTION). The concept is important in considering stellar energy transport from the core to the outer layers.

open cluster a group of stars which are relatively close together and move through space in association In an open cluster, as distinct from a GLOBULAR CLUSTER, the stars are only loosely bound by gravitation to each other and are subject to gravitational effects from the galaxy and other CLUSTERS. They are usually close to the plane of the galaxy, usually made up of a few hundred young stars; the Pliades and Hyades are examples.

open universe a model in cosmology in which the universe is without bounds, of infinite extent as opposed to a closed universe. It is not currently known whether the universe is open or closed; for it to be closed, the present observed expansion would have to slow down and eventually come to a halt, to be followed by a subsequent contraction. One factor currently thought to be of significance in seeking to resolve the problem is the total mass of the universe. Currently this is thought to be about one tenth of that required to ensure a closed universe. Other observations on the motions of stars, however, suggest that more mass must be present in the universe, perhaps in the form of DARK MATTER.

Ophelia a small, 50km diameter, satellite of Uranus. It is in a near circular orbit of radius about 54×10^3km.

Ophiuchus a constellation; usually regarded as of the northern sky, but cutting across the CELESTIAL EQUATOR. The brightest star in the 2nd magnitude Alpha Ophiuchi also known as Rasalhague. The constellation contains Barnard's star, the second closest to the Sun, as well as several GLOBULAR CLUSTERS, M10 or NGC6254 and M12 or NGC6218 amongst them.

opposition *see* **conjunction.**

optics the study of light; the definition is usually extended to include non-visible regions of the ELECTROMAGNETIC

SPECTRUM. The word is also used more loosely to refer to the lenses, mirrors, prisms, gratings etc. as used in optical instruments.

optical instrument any apparatus or instrument used for the study of light or for the investigation of bodies or phenomena by means of light. Often the definition is extended to include regions of the electromagnetic spectrum outwith the visible region, e.g., in radio telescopes.

orbit the path followed by a CELESTIAL BODY under the influence of all other bodies in space principally by their gravitational attraction. Most celestial bodies move in ELLIPTICAL ORBITS and their motion is as described by KEPLER'S LAWS.

orbital elements six quantities essential to specify the motions of, for instance, a planet under the gravitational attractions of the Sun. One possible set is as follows (i) the length of the major axis (ii) the ECCENTRICITY of the ELLIPSE (iii) the INCLINATION of the PLANE OF THE ORBIT to some reference plane on which a coordinate system is based (iv) the longitude of the ascending NODE on that coordinate system (v) the argument of PERIHELION i.e., the angle between the node and the direction of closest approach to the Sun (vi) an ANOMALY giving the position of the planet in its orbit at some EPOCH.

Orion a constellation on the CELESTIAL EQUATOR. The brightest stars are Alpha Orionis or Betelgeuse and Beta Orionis or Rigel. Contained within the constellation are the Orion nebula, M42 or NGC1976 and the Horsehead nebula.

Orion arm the spiral arm of the MILKY WAY GALAXY in which is the Sun. Maps of the galaxy using the 21cm line of hydrogen show the spiral nature of this, and other, arms.

Orionids a METEOR SHOWER seen in October which appears to come from a RADIANT in the Orion constellation.

Orion Nebula M42 or NGC 1976, an EMISSION NEBULA in the constellation Orion; it is also known as the Great Nebula in Orion. The emission is caused by intense ultraviolet light from new stars being formed in the nebula; the Trapezium, the multiple star Theta Orionis, lies at the centre of the nebula.

orrery a moving model of the components of the solar system; often driven by clockwork.

osculating elements the six quantities essential completely to specify the motion of, for instance, a PLANET under the GRAVITATIONAL ATTRACTION of the SUN above, all other gravitational influences being disregarded (*see also* ORBITAL ELEMENTS).

O star *see* **stellar classification.**

outer planets also known as giant planets, major planets or non-terrestrial planets; the planets beyond the asteroid belt; Jupiter, Saturn, Uranus Neptune and Pluto.

Ozma Project an attempt to detect artificial radio signals from two nearby stars, Tau Ceti and Epsilon Eridani, where there is some reason to suppose a planetary system exists. It did not succeed.

ozone a molecule consisting of three oxygen atoms, O_3. It is produced when ordinary oxygen molecules, O_2, are subjected ultraviolet radiation or electrical strains.

ozone layer also known as the ozonosphere, is a layer in the Earth's upper atmosphere at a height between 10 and 50 km where there is an appreciable concentration of OZONE formed by sunlight of very short wavelength ultraviolet. It acts as a screen absorbing much of the Sun's ultraviolet radiation which is harmful to most life forms. In the mid-1980s an "ozone hole" was found in the sky above the

Antarctic. It was traced to pollutants in the atmosphere assisting in the obstruction of, and inhibiting the production of, ozone. The hole has not diminished.

P

pair production the simultaneous conversion, within an atomic nucleus, of a gamma-ray high energy photon into an electron and positron.

Pallas a carbonaceous asteroid and the second to be discovered in 1802. It is the second largest asteroid with a mean diameter of 5.23 kilometres.

Pandora a small elongate satellite of Saturn with a length of approximately 110 kilometres.

parabola an open curve and one of the CONIC SECTIONS. In astronomy it is an orbit shape which may be assumed by a body moving around a central gravitational force (for example, a comet movung around the Sun). A *paraboloid* is created by rotating a parabola about its axis and this shape is often used for the mirror in reflecting telescopes.

parallax the apparent movement in the position of a heavenly body due in fact to a change in the position of the observer. It is therefore caused, in reality, by the Earth moving through space on its orbit. The distance of a heavenly body from Earth can be calculated by astronomers using parallax. The direction of the body from Earth is measured at two six month intervals when the Earth is at either side of its orbit. From the apparent change in position, the distance of the body from Earth can be deduced (see diagram on opposite page).

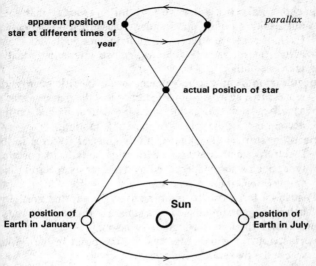

parallax

apparent position of star at different times of year

actual position of star

Sun

position of Earth in January

position of Earth in July

paraxial aligned close to the optical axis of a lens or similar system.

parsec (designated *pc*, and short for parallax second) a measure of distance in astronomy, which is equivalent to 3.26 light years or 3.086 ¥ 10¹³km.

particle horizon signifies the extremity of the universe from which light has reached us since expansion of the universe commenced—the 'visible universe'.

P Cygni a RECURRENT NOVA in the constellation Cygnus. Outbursts were recorded in the seventeenth century but since then its brightness has decreased gradually. The star is surrounded by what appears to be an expanding shell which on closer inspection was found to comprise three pulsating shells.

peculiar galaxy a collective term for any galaxy that doe not easily fit into the standard classification schemes Examples are relatively rare but include RING GALAXIES active, or interacting galaxies, (those interacting tidally with each other).

peculiar motion the movement of a specific star with respect to a nearby group of stars. Also, the part of a star': PROPER MOTION that is due to its movement in space afte accounting for the effects of the Sun's motion.

peculiar star any star that exhibits unusual features in it: spectrum when contrasted with most stars in its spectral type. Such a star is identified by a *p* after its spectral type and is often a type A or B star.

Pegasus a large constellation near Cygnus in the northern hemisphere distinguished by a square of its brightest stars

penumbra the lighter fringe of a sunspot.

periastron in a binary star system, the point in the orbits where the two stars are closest to each other.

pericentre in an orbit, the point that is nearest the centre of mass of the whole system.

perigee in the orbit of the Moon or an artificial satellite around the Earth, the point at which the two bodies are closest together and the satellite reaches its maximum velocity.

perihelion in the orbit of a planet about the Sun, the point at which the planet is closest to the Sun.

period the time gap between successive events in a regularly occurring phenomenon e.g., the period of rotation of a planet, or the period of a binary star which is the time taken by the companion to orbit the primary.

period-luminosity relation a graphical plot of luminosity against time for stars of the Cepheid variable type (pulsating variable yellow giants).

Perseids an annual meteor shower which peaks on August 12th. It is a major shower and one of the most reliable with a recorded history of about two thousand years.

Perseus a large constellation in the northern hemisphere lying in the Milky Way, and containing the variable star Algol. It also contains two open CLUSTERS called the Double Cluster which can be seen without instruments.

Perseus Arm the spiral arms of the Galaxy (MILKY WAY) contain dense clouds of interstellar dust and gas in which young stars are found. The Perseus Arm is one part of the spiral reaching from beyond the galactic centre to the region beyond the Sun.

perturbation an interruption in the normal motion of a body due to a localized gravitational disturbance. A typical example is a comet under the gravitational influence of the Sun which may experience perturbations if it passes near enough to a planet for that planet's gravitational influence to be sufficiently large to affect the comet's motion. This is particularly true for a massive planet such as Jupiter.

Phaethon a six kilometre diameter asteroid, discovered in 1983 which may be the nucleus of a former comet. It is thought to be the parent of the Geminids meteor shower.

phase the visible, illuminated surface of the Moon or a planet at a certain time in its orbit and the ratio of the illuminated area to the area of the objects apparent disc (which is taken as circular). The phase of the Moon as seen from the Earth depends on the relative position of the two bodies and the Sun, since the Moon is visible only by reflected sunlight.

phase angle the angle created between two lines, one of which joins the Sun to a planet, the other joining the Earth to the planet.

Phobos one of the two small satellites of Mars discovered in 1877. Phobos is the larger of the two and is vaguely elongated measuring approximately 27 by 22km. It has a cratered surface and one crater (Stickney) is 10 kilometres in diameter.

Phoebe the outermost of Saturn's satellites. It is a rough sphere 220km in diameter and has a very dark surface. It was discovered in 1898.

photometry the measurement of a star's MAGNITUDE (brightness) within certain wavelength bands, and the variation over time. Certain properties of the star e.g., temperature, can be assumed from such measurements. Photometry uses photoelectric instruments (*see* PHOTOMULTIPLIER) and can be used for a single star, or a particular angle of sky with several stars.

photomultiplier a device used in PHOTOMETRY which consists of a photocathode (an electrode that emits electrons when struck by electromagnetic radiation) that gives off electrons when light falls on it. By a process of amplification, whereby the released electrons strike electrodes releasing further electrons, the signal is enhanced and output.

photon a quantum of energy is the form of electromagnetic radiation which can be thought of as a particle of light energy, the energy increasing as the wavelength shortens.

photosphere the Sun's (or a star's) visible surface and the part from which the visible light is radiated. It is about 500 kilometres thick and has a temperature of 6000K which falls to 4000K at the interface with the CHROMOSPHERE. The photosphere is the region of a solar activity within which are FLARES, SUNSPOTS and similar phenomena.

Pisces a faint, though large, zodiac constellation near PEGASUS.

Planck's constant (designated h) or the constant of proportionality is the ratio of the energy and frequency of a photon. It is used in the equation $E=hv=hc/$ (Planck's law), where E is the energy of the photon, v is the frequency of the wave and the wavelength while c is the speed of light in a vacuum. Planck's constant has a value $6.261 \ 10^{-34}$ joule seconds, and it is used in calculations in quantum theory.

planet the name given originally to seven heavenly bodies that were thought to move among the stars, the latter being stationary. It is now defined as an astronomical body that orbits the Sun (or other star) and shines by reflected light only. The inner planets of the solar system are essentially rocky (Mercury, Venus, Earth and Mars) while the outer planets (Jupiter, Saturn, Uranus and Neptune) are essentially gaseous. These, with Pluto form the major planets. Numerous asteroids form the minor planets. Observations of other stars suggest there may be other planetary systems.

planetarium the instrument (and also the enclosing building) which enables an artificial night sky to be projected onto the domed ceiling of the building. The motion of the planet, moons and positions of stars can be displayed.

planetary nebula a shell of gas around a star. The gas expands outwards during the later stages of stellar evolution when the star is dying. (Contrary to its name, there is no connection with a planet). Such nebulae form when a RED GIANT loses mass in the process of finally becoming a WHITE DWARF. The shell of gas is ionized by the remaining hot core and moves outwards for 30 to 40,000 years until the material becomes dispersed. The nebulae may be disc-shaped, or resemble an hourglass (dumbbell) shape e.g., Ring, and Dumbbell Nebulae, and approximately 1,500 are known in the Galaxy.

planetary rings the ring-like structures composed of dust particles and small bodies that surround the four large planets: Jupiter, Saturn, Uranus and Neptune. Most of the material lies within the ROCHE LIMITS. The rings of Jupiter, Uranus and Neptune are much fainter than those of Saturn and were discovered relatively recently. Uranus has nine rings while Neptune has two major rings and other ring-like features that are less definite.

Saturn has by far the best developed and most complex ring system which was seen initially by Galileo in 1610. A number of rings are now known to exist and these have been identified A to G and they consist of ice and dust with a size variation from centimetres to a few metres. There are other features including numerous ringlets and some gaps between rings have been identified specifically e.g., the Cassini Division separates the A and B rings (*see also* Saturn).

planet X the planet in the solar system which as yet exists only in theory. It is thought to be beyond Pluto and indicated by discrepancies in orbits of the outer planets. It was predicted before the discovery of Pluto but this planet is small in comparison to the postulated mass of planet X which is seven times that of Earth.

planisphere a star map that is two-dimensional and a projection of part of the celestial sphere. By using a movable overlay it can show the visible stars at a certain time, for a given range of latitude.

plasma essentially a high temperature gas of charged particles (electrons and ions) rather than neutral atoms or molecules. A plasma is electrically neutral overall but the presence of charged particles means that it can support an electric current. It is formed in stars at very high temperatures and it occurs in the interstellar medium and MAGNETOSPHERES. Plasmas can be affected by magnetic or electric fields because they are composed of charged particles.

plasmasphere a region of cold plasma lying around the Earth, within the magnetosphere and above the ionosphere. The particles are primarily electrons and protons generated by ultraviolet radiation and X-rays from the Sun acting on molecules.

Pleiades an open cluster of many hundred stars in the constellation Taurus. Six are visible to the unaided eye contradicting the popular name of the Seven Sisters. It is 400 light years away and faint REFLECTION NEBULAE are seen around the brighter stars.

Plough comprises a group of the brightest stars in the constellation Ursa Major. Due to the PROPER MOTION of two of the seven stars, the shape of the Plough changes very slowly over time. In North America it is called the Big Dipper.

Pluto the ninth and smallest planet in the SOLAR SYSTEM and the one that lies farthest away from the SUN. The existence of Pluto was predicted by an American astronomer called Percival Lowell from the behaviour of the orbits of its closest neighbours, NEPTUNE and URANUS. Pluto was finally spotted in 1930, fourteen years after Lowell died. Pluto appears as a tiny speck when viewed from Earth and little is known about it, but it probably has an iron core and a rocky surface with a covering of methane ice. Since it is so far from the Sun (a maximum of 7,338 million kilometres), it must be extremely cold, in the region of −230°C. A day on Pluto lasts for almost seven Earth days and a year is 248.4 Earth years. At the equator, the planet has a diameter in the region of 3,500km. Pluto has a wide elliptical orbit which sometimes brings it closer to the Sun. In 1989, it was at its closest point to the Sun (called its *perihelion*), but this only occurs every 248 years. During this phase of its orbit, Pluto apparently has a thin atmosphere composed of methane gas. However, when it moves away from the Sun again it is possible that this becomes frozen once again. In 1979 it was discovered that Pluto has one small satellite (which was named *Charon*), which is about a quarter the size of Pluto. The two bodies effectively form a double planet system.

Pointers two stars in the PLOUGH which when joined by a line, point towards the Pole star.

polar axis one of two axes of rotation for an equatorial mounting telescope. This axis parallels the Earth's axis and points to the celestial poles.

polar caps a circular area around the pole region of a planet. More specifically, the area of ice and snow at the poles of a planet such as Earth. On Mars, the caps contain ice and frozen carbon dioxide.

Polaris (Alpha Ursa Minoris) the brightest star in the constellation Ursa Minor. It is a Cepheid variable and the present pole star.

polar motion *see* **Chandler wobble.**

Pollux (Beta Geminorum) the brightest star, and an orange giant (type K) in the constellation Gemini.

Population I one of two divisions of stars and clusters introduced in 1944 by W. Baade. Population I stars are those thought to be relatively young and which occur in the spiral arms of galaxies e.g., open clusters, MAIN-SEQUENCE stars, SUPERGIANTS and interstellar gas and dust. The stars have high *metallicity* that is a relatively high metal content as a result of NUCLEOSYNTHESIS. Although Population I and II stars differ, there is a gradation between the two and Population I can be divided into young (or *extreme*) such as T-Tauri stars, and older, e.g., the Sun.

Population II one of two divisions of stars and clusters (*see* POPULATION I) which contains relatively old objects. These stars and star clusters are found in a halo around the galactic centre. They contain less of the heavier elements (that is heavier than helium) and occupy elliptical orbits inclined to the galactic plane. This group is also divided into two, the older *halo* population II (e.g., GLOBULAR CLUSTERS) formed from the original gas cloud which on further contraction led to *intermediate* population II stars formed in an extended disc. Contraction of the disc further produced the *disc population* stars, an intermediate group comprising young population II or old population I stars, such as PLANETARY NEBULAE.

Population III a theoretical third class of stars comprising supermassive stars that might have predated formation of the galaxies.

Portia one of the small satellites of Uranus. It was discovered in 1986.

position angle the angle which states the orientation of one celestial body with respect to another. It is measured in degrees (0 to 360) moving easterly from the north.

positional astronomy *see* **astrometry.**

positron a particle with the same mass as an electron but a positive electrical charge - the antiparticle of an electron. Positrons are produced during decay processes and are themselves annihilated on passing through matter.

Poynting-Roberston effect small interplanetary particles that orbit the Sun absorb solar radiation and then radiate energy back out in all directions. The effect of this process is to reduce the kinetic energy of the particles and they move in ever decreasing orbits around the Sun, spiralling in to the centre. This is the Poynting-Robertson effect, but for very small particles it is countered by RADIATION PRESSURE which ejects them from the solar system.

preceding as an object moves across the sky because of the Earth's rotation, the leading edge of a planet or feature is termed preceding. The edge that follows is termed *trailing* or *following*.

precession a rotating body precesses when the application of a couple (two equal and opposite parallel forces) with an axis at right angles to the axis of rotation causes the body to turn around the third, common, perpendicular axis (as seen with a gyroscope). In astronomy, the turning force is supplied by external gravitational forces. The Earth is affected by the Sun and Moon and its precession results in a cone being traced out by its axis of rotation; similarly a circle is traced out by the celestial poles. The time period involved is almost 26,000 years.

prime focus the point at which incident light from the primary mirror in a reflecting telescope focuses. The prime focus is in the incident path and in large telescopes, further instruments may be sited here.

prime meridian the circle of zero longitude on a planet, which is also a great circle.

primeval fireball an early phase of the universe which was swamped with high energy radiation. The cosmic microwave background is intepreted as radiation from this time which has cooled and expanded.

prismatic astrolabe an instrument used to determine accurately the positions of stars. It comprises essentially a telescope in front of which is placed a prism and an artificial horizon which create a double image. A reading is taken when the two images coincide.

Procyon (Alpha Canis Minoris) the brightest star of the Canis Minor constellation. It is the fifth brightest star in the sky and is actually a binary system consisting of the primary, an F star and the companion, a white dwarf.

Prometheus a satellite of Saturn that was discovered in 1980 with another, Pandora. It is very small measuring only 70 by 40km.

prominence a cloud or flame-like structure in the Sun's CORONA or CHROMOSPHERE. They are denser and cooler than their surroundings and are seen as bright features in the corona and dark filaments against the brighter disc. Prominences are categorised into *active* and *quiescent*; the former are associated with SUNSPOTS and FLARES and last only a little time, changing rapidly and commonly show a surge or spray form. Quiescent prominences are stable for months and may be tens of thousands or a few hundred thousand kilometres long. There is also an intermediate form—*active-region filaments* which are long lived but show a flow along their length.

proper motion (designated) the combination of the true motion of a star in space and the relative motion of the solar system to produce an apparent motion for the star across the celestial sphere.

Proteus Neptune's second largest satellite which was discovered in 1989.

protogalaxy a gas cloud that condenses in the initial stages of evolution of a galaxy.

proton a particle that carries a positive charge and is found in the NUCLEUS of every ATOM. As an atom is electrically neutral, the number of protons equals the number of negatively charged ELECTRONS. Although the mass of a

proton (1.673 10^{-27}kg) is far greater than the mass of a
electron (9.11 10^{-31}kg), their charges are equal i
magnitude. The number of protons in the nucleus of a
atom (the atomic number) is identical for any one elemen
and is used to classify elements in the Periodic Table. Fo
example, as every oxygen atom contains 6 protons, it ha
an atomic number of 6 in the periodic table, whereas every
gold atom contains 79 protons and thus has an atomic
number and periodic table position of 79.

proton-proton chain a primary source of energy in stars
Through a series of nuclear fusion reactions hydrogen i:
converted into helium with the release of energy which
maintains the core temperature.

protoplanet a body in the process of evolving into a planet
by means of ACCRETION.

protostar one of the earliest stages seen in stars formation,
when it is fragmenting and condensing from an interstellar
gas cloud but before sufficient collapse has occurred to
permit nuclear reactions in the core.

Proxima Centauri a small, faint red star which is the
closest one to the SOLAR SYSTEM (some 4.3 light years
away) yet to be discovered. It occurs in the constellation of
Centaurus and is the third and smallest member of a series
of three stars called *Alpha Centauri*. It takes about a million
years for it to orbit the other two stars which are larger and
brighter. Proxima Centauri occasionally burns more
brightly for short periods of time but is usually quite dim.

Ptolemaic system an early model of planetary motion
within the solar system described by Ptolemy, a Greek
astronomer, during the second century. It was a geocentric
model with the Earth orbited by the Moon and the known
planets, and it was the accepted wisdom until adoption of
the Copernican System, in the mid-sixteenth century.

P-type asteroid a common type of asteroid thought to have organic-rich surfaces.

Puck an almost spherical satellite of Uranus. It has a diameter of approximately 150 kilometres and was discovered in 1985.

pulsar a rapidly rotating neutron star which is similar to the Sun in mass, but has a diameter of approximately ten kilometres. Pulsars emit regular bursts of radio waves at a high frequency, from a few seconds to milliseconds. The first pulsars discovered were radio emitters and over 500 are now known, but there are pulsars emitting X-rays or gamma rays.

All single star pulsars are slowing down in their emissions as they lose rotational energy. There are also binary systems which emit X-rays. Due to complex gas transfer and resulting dynamic effects, these pulsars speed up.

The central star of the Crab nebula is the youngest known pulsar and one of the brightest gamma-ray sources. It has a period of 33 milliseconds which is slowing at the rate of one millionth per day. It is thought that pulsars form in SUPERNOVA explosions.

pulsating star a variable star that pulsates, periodically dimming and brightening. A star pulsates due to internal instability caused by the antagonistic action of gravity (inwards) and expansion (outwards). When it expands beyond a certain point, the change is reversed by gravity. Examples are RR Lyrae and most Cepheid stars.

pyrheliometer an instrument that measures the heat energy from the Sun over a given time and area.

Q

Q-type asteriod a rare asteroid type with similarities to meteorites known as CHONDRITES.

Quadrantids a meteor shower with its RADIANT in the constellation Boötes which occurs annually early in January. It is a narrow, rather variable stream of meteors with a diameter of approximately 1.7 million kilometres.

quantum gravity an attempt, and as yet undeveloped theory, to combine *Grand Unified Theory* (i.e., a single theory of nuclear and electromagnetic forces) with a theory of gravitational interaction. A single unified theory would enable all physical interactions to be described in a unified set of equations.

quantum numbers a set of four numbers used to describe atomic structures. The principal quantum number (n) defines the shells (or orbits) which are visualized as orbitals (that is, a charge cloud which represents the probability distribution of an electron). The orbit nearest the nucleus has 2 electrons and $n = 1$. The second shell contains 8 electrons (and $n = 2$) and so on, the maximum number of electrons in each shell being defined by the formula $2n^2$. The orbital quantum number (l) defines the shape of the orbits and these are designated s, p, d and f, the letters arising purely for historical reasons. The magnetic orbital quantum number (m) sets the position of the orbit within a magnetic field and s is the spin quantum number. The latter is based upon the assumption that no two electrons may be exactly alike and pairs of electrons are considered to have opposite spin.

The quantum numbers *n, l* and *m* are related and allow the electronic structure of any atom to be determined.

quark any of the theoretical building blocks that participate in the strong interactive forces between elementary particles. Quarks are thought to be the units from which most other particles are formed, and under standard temperature and pressure only exist with other quarks as pairs or triplets to form hadrons (including neutrons and protons). Quarks have been linked to the condensed matter found in the depths of neutron stars, where it is postulated they may exist in the 'free' state.

quasar a small 'quasi-stellar' object (which on contraction produces the name quasar) that emits an enormous amount of energy, mainly as infrared radiation. They also emit X-rays and about one tenth are radio sources. Quasars are compact sources and have the largest REDSHIFTS found, a feature which has made them important in astronomy, as they are the most distant observable objects at up to 10^9 light years away. An apparent paradox is that although quasars generate enormous quantities of energy, the light-producing area is only one light-day, or less, across. The explanation is that the energy source is the falling of matter into a vast BLACK HOLE, at the centre of the quasar.

From the early identifications in the 1960s, thousands of quasars have been catalogued.

quiet Sun the term applied to the Sun when its sunspot cycle is at its minimum.

R

radar astronomy the transmission of high frequency radio signals to bodies within the solar system. Faint reflections from these bodies are received on Earth and the time between the transmission of the signal and reception of its reflection can be transformed into a measure of distance. The technique has been used to detect meteor showers, to map distances (and in imparting a value to the astronomical unit) and map planetary features, and also to calculate the period of rotation of a planet.

radial velocity otherwise known as the line-of-sight velocity because it is the velocity of a star or similar object along the observer's line of sight. This is not the body's true velocity which can only be calculated if the transverse velocity is known (i.e., the velocity *across* the line of sight). Most stars have radial velocities between +40 and -40 kilometres per second (a positive valve means the star is receding).

radian an alternative to the degree when measuring angles. It is the angle subtended at the centre of a circle by an arc that is equal in length to the radius. There are 2 radians in 360° and one radian is roughly 57.3°.

radiant the apparent origin of meteor showers on the CELESTIAL SPHERE. It is identified by the trails of meteors emanating from this point.

radiation belt the region around a planet in which are trapped charged particles (electrons and protons). The belt is shaped much like a doughnut and the particles follow spiral paths, trapped by the magnetic field of the plant. The particles originate from the solar wind or from particle collisions between atoms/ions in the atmosphere and cosmic rays. The major planets all have such belts and those of the Earth are called the VAN ALLEN RADIATION BELTS.

radiation pressure the pressure created by photons (such as light or other electromagnetic radiation) on a surface. The pressure generated by the transfer of momentum from the radiation to the surface is very small indeed and quite unnoticed on large particles. However, it is significant on very small particles, such as grains of dust, and radiation pressure from the Sun pushes very small particles away from the solar system.

radio astronomy the study of the universe by means of radio waves emitted by various bodies. The frequency of the waves varies enormously from 10 megahertz to 300 gigahertz and they are emitted by pulsars, quasars, radiogalaxies, remnants of supernovae, the Sun and Jupiter, interstellar ions and cosmic microwave background.

radio galaxy a galaxy that is the origin of radio emissions in the form of SYNCHROTRON RADIATION from electrons that are travelling close to the speed of light. Cygnus A is a typical example.

radio interferometer a type of RADIO TELESCOPE in which an object is observed by more than one antenna. The distribution of radio emissions from the sources is reflected in the analysed signals and by moving the settings of the interferometer, a radio brightness map can be generated.

radiometer a device for measuring the electromagnetic

radiation from an object, whether infrared radiation or radio emissions.

radio source an origin of natural radio emissions which can be detected with a radio telescope. Radio sources include the Sun, Jupiter, PULSARS, QUASARS, RADIO GALAXIES, spiral galaxies, remnants of SUPERNOVAE etc. There is also a background of synchrotron radiation from galactic cosmic rays which may affect the sensitivity of radio telescopes. The distribution in space of the emissions from a radio source is called the radio-source structure and extragalactic sources often feature two bright *lobes* at some distance from the optical position of the galaxy.

radio telescope the instrument used to detect and analyse radio waves, by means of an antenna which then feeds into an amplifier and detector. The antenna may take the form of a dish and separate units often make up a radio interferometer to provide the necessary angular resolution. Individual radio telescopes will differ because they may be used to study different types of the spectrum.

radio waves electromagnetic radiation with frequencies in the radio range of the spectrum, from 20 kilohertz to about 300 gigahertz. Such radiation can be transmitted through space with no intermediate physical link and radio waves can be used to carry sound, pictures and digital data.

In radio astronomy, certain frequency bands are set aside to limit interference.

Ras Algethi (alpha herculis) a binary star and the brightest in the constellation Hercules comprising a red supergiant (type M star). Its companion is a yellow giant which appears green (type F).

Rayleigh scattering *see* **scattering.**

recombination the process whereby a free electron combines with an ion in an ionized gas. As it does so energy is released as electromagnetic radiation, photons, that correspond to particular wavelengths firstly as the electron is bound to the ion and then as it passes down and between energy levels within the atom. *Recombination lines* are the spectra created by this process in, for example, EMISSION NEBULAE.

recurrent nova a star that undergoes an explosive event producing dramatic and sudden increases in brightness and which shows periodic outbursts. A recurrent nova differs from a classical nova in that the brightness change is smaller and its decline is swifter. The gap between events is commonly 10-80 years. The nova is actually a binary system comprising a WHITE DWARF and a RED GIANT. The red giant loses matter very quickly and hydrogen builds up on the surface of the white dwarf and this results in a thermonuclear explosion periodically.

red dwarf a MAIN-SEQUENCE STAR (usually M or K type) which is cooler and smaller than the Sun and which generates a magnetic field. The magnetic field initiates phenomena such as flares, coronae and hot CHROMOSPHERES.

red giant an ageing, evolved star that has expanded greatly and has used up about 10% of its hydrogen. The outer layers become cooler than the hot centre and it therefore appears red. As the hydrogen is consumed in nuclear fusion, the core collapses becoming inert, and around it the combustion of hydrogen recommences in a shell, causing a massive expansion of the outer layers and also cooling (surface temperature about 4,000K). Red giants are very luminous still because although the temperature is lower, there is a vast area emitting heat e.g., *Aldebaran* is 35 times larger than the Sun. The Sun will eventually become a red giant in about 5,000 million years, at which

time it will expand until its diameter is roughly the same
as the Earth's orbit.

red shift the displacement of spectral lines towards the red
end of the spectrum in light observed from certain
galaxies. This is interpreted as being due to the DOPPLER
EFFECT and indicates that the galaxies are receding into
space. This increase in the wavelength of the
electromagnetic radiation may also be caused by the
presence of a gravitational field.

reflection the property of certain surfaces whereby rays of
light (or other wave motion) striking the surface are
returned (reflected) in accordance with definite laws. The
incoming, incident, ray becomes the reflected ray and
these, with the normal (the perpendicular line at the point
of incidence/reflection) all lie in the same place. Also the
angle made by the two rays with the normal, is equal. A
smooth surface reflects in a regular fashion while a rough
surface results in a diffuse reflection.

reflection nebula a cloud of interstellar gas and dust that is
close to a star. The light from the star is reflected and
scattered by the particles and creates the effect of the
cloud being luminous. The scattered light is essentially the
same as that of the star although blue light is scattered
more than red because the effect differs with wavelength.
Such nebula are seen surrounding stars of the Pleiades
cluster.

refraction the bending of a ray of light or other wave
motion on travelling from one medium to another. The
refraction occurs at the interface between the media and is
caused by the light travelling at different velocities in the
different media. The incident ray becomes the refracted
ray which with the normal (the perpendicular line at the
point of incidence/refraction) all lie in the same place.

Regulus (Alpha Leonis) a triple star and the brightest in the constellation Leo.

relativistic the term applied to anything travelling at a velocity close to that of light. At such velocities, the special theory of relativity is used in associated calculations.

relativity is the theory developed by Einstein and which is made up of two parts. The *special theory* states that the speed of light is the same for all observers, whatever their speed, that is light from an object travels at the same velocity whether the object is moving or stationary. Nothing may move faster than the speed of light. Further important implications of this theory are that the mass of a body is a function of its speed, and Einstein derived the *mass-energy equation, $E = mc^2$* where c is the speed of light. As a result of this theory the concept of *time dilation* was proposed which essentially means that for someone travelling at very great speed, time passes much more slowly for them than it does for a stationary observer.

The *general theory of relativity* relates to gravity. Matter in space is said to cause space to curve so as to set up a gravitational field and gravitation becomes a property of space. The validity of Einstein's theories has been tested with experiments in modern atomic physics.

remote sensing is the collection of a variety of information without contact with the object of study. This includes aerial photography from both aircraft and satellites and the use of infrared, ultraviolet and microwave radiation emitted from the object, e.g., an individual site, part of a town, crop and forest patterns. Another type of remote sensing involves the production of an impulse of light, or radar, which is reflected by the object and the image is then captured on film or tape.

Using these various techniques, large areas of the ground can be studied and surprisingly sharp pictures obtained which can be used in many ways. Remote sensing is used in numerous disciplines including agriculture and forestry, civil engineering, geology, geography and archaeology. In addition, it is possible to create pictures with a remarkable amount of detail which would otherwise take a very long time to collect. It is also applied to other bodies in the solar system with images and data gathered by orbiting satellites.

residual the discrepancy between an observed valve or quantity (such as the position of a comet) and the predicted, calculated value. The difference may be due to errors in observation or prediction or limited accuracy in the observation.

resolution a measure of the smallest detail that can be distinguished with a telescope or other imaging instrument.

resolving power the ability of a telescope or similar instrument to distinguish detail.

resonance the phenomenon responsible for COMMENSURABLE orbits and the divisions in the rings of Saturn. It is due to an external disturbance or stimulus with a particular frequency which coincides with the natural frequency of the system affected, producing an additional response.

rest mass the mass of a particle at rest, usually measured in megaelectron volts.

retrograde the east-west movement of an object on the celestial sphere or clockwise movement (when viewed from the north) in an orbit or around an axis within the solar system,

Rhea a satellite of Saturn and the second largest with a diameter of 1,530km. The surface is heavily cratered and icy.

Rigel (Beta Orionis) a supergiant and luminous star (type B) that is the brightest in the constellation Orion. It is at least 60,000 times more luminous than the Sun.

right ascension (designated) a coordinate used, with others, in specifying positions on the CELESTIAL SPHERE. It is equivalent to longitude on Earth and is measured in hours, minutes and seconds from 0 to 24 hours, where 15° of arc equates to one hour.

ring galaxy a very rare galaxy that is shaped like a ring, sometimes with a nucleus situated off-centre. It has been postulated that the origin is a collision between two galaxies where one passes through the other producing a shock wave of interstellar gas in the form of a ring in which star formation occurs.

Ring nebula a bright ring-shaped PLANETARY NEBULA in the constellation Lyra. The slightly elliptical ring has a star in the centre and a radius of approximately one third of a light year.

Roche limit the minimum distance between a body and a satellite at which the latter can stay in equilibrium and remain stable. If the satellite is held together only by gravitational attraction and if it is the same density as the major body, then the distance is almost two and a half times the radius of the plant. A satellite which also possesses tensile strength, e.g., rock, can exist within the limit; without such strength, the satellite would be destroyed by tidal forces.

Roche lobes two drop-shaped surfaces which meet at their points to resemble an hourglass and which are found in BINARY STAR systems. The surface is generated by points at zero gravity due to the pull on a particle of both stars being equal. Where the lobes touch in the centre, where the gravity is also zero, is called the inner Lagrangian point.

Depending upon the state of the stars in the binary, the Roche lobes may fill with material and there may be transfer between stars in adjacent lobes.

rotation one complete turn of a body about its axis. Also the spinning of a galaxy or bodies held together by gravity.

rotation curve the graphical plot showing the velocity of rotation of a galaxy against the distance from the centre. Moving away from the centre, the velocity increases rapidly and then levels out through the rest of the galaxy. This data enables the total mass of a galaxy to be estimated.

r-process a NUCLEOSYNTHETIC process which is rapid (hence r-process) and occurs in SUPERNOVA explosions when there is a high flux of neutrons. It is the process by which the heavier elements are thought to have been produced naturally and involves a nucleus rapidly capturing two or more neutrons. Any intermediate decay to an unstable isotope is prevented by the rapid process and subsequent explusion of beta particles leaves a stable, neutron-rich element.

RR Lyrae stars a group of pulsating VARIABLE STARS found mainly in globular clusters. They are old POPULATION II stars with moderate luminosity and a reasonably constant absolute magnitude renders them useful in indicators of distance.

RS Canum Venaticorum Star a variable BINARY STAR (a sub-giant and MAIN SEQUENCE star, usually both type G) that exhibits high activity such as FLARES, star-spots and CORONAE. The sub-giant rotates more quickly than usual creating strong magnetic features and the associated activity.

R star a spectral type of red giant star which is now included in the CARBON STARS.

R-type asteroid an asteroid with quite high ALBEDO, eg DEMBOWSKA. It is a rare type of asteroid.

runaway star a young star that has an unusually high velocity through space, e.g., 53 Arietis and AE Aurigae. It is postulated that such stars were once part of a binary system and following the SUPERNOVA explosion of an associated star, the runaway star was catapulted into space.

RV Tauri star one of a group of yellow giants, pulsating variable stars of types F, G or K. Such stars may be forerunners to planetary nebulae and some are found in GLOBULAR CLUSTERS.

S

Sagitta (The Arrow) The third smallest CONSTELLATION lying in the MILKY WAY in the northern hemisphere near to Cygnus. It was described and listed by Ptolemy in AD140 and lies near to Aquilla. It has two bright stars, Gamma and Delta, of 3rd magnitude and some of 4th magnitude. It also contains a GLOBULAR CLUSTER M71.

Sagittarius (The Archer) A large ZODIAC CONSTELLATION in the southern hemisphere, lying near Scorpius and partly in the MILKY WAY. It is the most southern of the zodiac constellations and is very extensive containing many complex phenomena. The centre of the Galaxy lies in the constellation Sagittarius and the brightest stars are Kaus Australis, 1.8 magnitude and Nunki, 2.0 magnitude. There are several others of 2nd and 3rd magnitude and other phenomena include GLOBULAR CLUSTERS such as M22 and M25, NEBULAE, including the Omega, Trifid and Lagoon nebulae, star clouds and OPEN CLUSTERS. It also contains a complex of radio sources at the galactic centre called SAGITTARIUS A.

Sagittarius A The overall name for a complex of radio sources associated with the centre of the GALAXY, with Sagittarius A being one of these sources. There are two parts, Sagittarius A West and Sagittarius A East. Sagittarius A West is a source of thermal radiation and is spiral shaped containing ionized gas and dust. It contains a highly compact, intense radio source, Sagittarius A*,

which lies at the galactic centre and may be a BLACK HOLE.
Sagittarius A East is believed to be the remnant of a
SUPERNOVA and is a source of non-thermal radiation.

Saha equations a set of equations derived by M.N. Saha, an
Indian physicist, which are useful in the study of star
spectra and atmospheres. The equations relate the
numbers of ions (charged particles) to the number of
neutral atoms in all of the ionization states (i.e., X^+, X^{2+},
X^{3+} etc.), for a particular atom. It indicates a greater
ionization with rise in temperature and enables the
numbers of atoms (whether neutral, X^+, X^{2+}, etc.), in stars
of known temperatures to be determined.

SAO star catalogue The Smithsonian Astrophysical
Observatory Star Catalog, listing 259,000 stars, which
was published in 1966.

satellite A natural satellite is a heavenly body or moon
which orbits around a PLANET. An artificial satellite is a
man made object launched into orbit around the Earth,
moon or other heavenly body. They are used for a variety
of scientific purposes and for communications and are
usually not manned.

satellite galaxy A small galaxy which orbits a large massive
one e.g. MAGELLANIC CLOUDS.

Saturn one of the four *gas giants,* the second largest planet
and sixth in the SOLAR SYSTEM, with an orbit between that
of JUPITER and URANUS. Saturn has a diameter at the equator
of about 120,800 kilometres and is a maximum distance of
1,507,000,000 kilometres from the SUN. Saturn rotates
very fast and this causes it to flatten at its poles and bulge
at the equator. A day on Saturn lasts for $10^{1}/_{4}$ hours and a
year, (or one complete orbit of the Sun), for 29.45 Earth
years. Saturn is a cold planet of frozen gases and ice and
has a surface temperature in the region of -170°C. It is

mainly gaseous with an outer zone of hydrogen and helium over a metallic hydrogen layer and a core of ice silicate. The atmosphere is rich in methane and ethane. Saturn is well-known for its *rings* which are, in fact, ice particles and other debris thought to be the remains of a SATELLITE which broke up close to the planet. The rings are wide, in the region of 267,876 kilometres across, but they are extremely thin (only a few kilometres). The *Voyager* space probes approached close to Saturn in 1980 and 1981 and photographs taken revealed that there were many more rings than had previously been detected. They are brighter than those of any other planet.

Saturn has 24 satellites or moons, some of which were discovered by the *Voyager* spacecraft, including *Atlas, Prometheus* and *Calypso. Titan* is the largest moon and, at 5,200 kilometres diameter, is larger than Mercury. It is the only moon known to have a detectable atmosphere, a layer of gases above its surface.

Saturn nebula *see* **Aquarius.**

scattering Deflection of the component particles (photons, electrons) of light or other ELECTROMAGNETIC RADIATION due to collision with other particles (atoms, molecules, nuclei) in the matter through which they are travelling. One such form is COMPTON SCATTERING (Compton effect), in which a photon collides with an electrically charged particle. The photon loses some of its energy to the charged particle and is scattered with less energy (longer wavelength) than before the interaction. The particle has greater energy than before. Rayleigh scattering occurs when the particles, such as dust, in the medium through which the light rays are travelling are smaller than the wavelength of the light. The scattering is by diffraction and is dependent upon wavelength. Blue light is more effectively scattered by small particles than red light. Cosmic dust may cause light form stars to be reddened due to scattering of blue lights (interstellar reddening). The rising or setting sun similarly appears reddened due to the presence of dust in a thick atmosphere.

scintillation the twinkling effect of star light caused by rapid alterations in brightness (amplitude) due to scattering by refraction in the Earth's atmosphere. Radio waves from various celestial bodies are also subject to scintillations caused by variations in refraction in the Earth's IONOSPHERE (ionospheric scintillations), in the interstellar medium (interstellar scintillations) and in the interplanetary medium (interplanetary scintillations)

Scorpius (The Scorpion) An extensive, prominent and bright ZODIAC CONSTELLATION lying partly in the MILKY WAY and within the southern hemisphere. It was first described and listed in AD140 by Ptolemy and contains several interesting phenomena including an X-ray source called Scorpius x-1, bright open clusters (M6 and M7) and GLOBULAR CLUSTERS (M80 and M4). There are two stars of 1st magnitude, Shaula (λ) which is a blue SUBGIANT, and Antares (α). A number of other bright stars are present of 2nd and 3rd magnitude.

Scorpius-x-1 The first stellar X-ray source to be discovered (in 1962) and also the brightest, lying in the CONSTELLATION of SCORPIUS in the southern hemisphere. It was subsequently identified as emanating from a variable BINARY STAR of low mass, V818 Sco, the X-ray source (thought to be a NEUTRON star) being designated Sco X-1.

Sculptor (The Sculptor's workshop) a faint CONSTELLATION lying in the southern hemisphere near Grus (The Crane) which is not readily detectable. It contains a bright variable star, R-Sculptoris and its four brightest stars are of 4th magnitude. The south GALACTIC POLE lies within this constellation which was first described in the 1700s by Nicholas L.de Lacaille.

Scutum (The Shield) A small CONSTELLATION lying in the MILKY WAY in the southern hemisphere, near SAGITTARIUS. It contains some stars of 4th magnitude brightness and R Scuti, which is a bright RV TAURI STAR. This is the prototype of a type called Delta Scuti a class of young variable pulsating stars in which the light curve varies in shape and amplitude. Another interesting phenomenon within Scutum is an open STAR CLUSTER called The Wild Duck (M11), as well as many other clusters of stars.

secular changing or continuing over an extended period of time.

secular acceleration the gradual apparent increase in the velocity of the orbit of the Moon around the Earth which has been measured as 10.3 arc seconds every century. It is caused by tidal interaction or friction between the Moon and the Earth and the gravitational pull exerted by the other planets.

secular parallax the ongoing increase in the angular displacement of stars over a period of time due to the movement of the Sun through space. It is used to calculate the distance of star groups which are nearby. The calculation assumes that random movements of individual stars tend to cancel each other out and they are more or less at the same distance from the Sun. The secular parallax is measured relative to the LOCAL STANDARD OF REST and increases by the Sun's velocity of 19.5kms^{-1} which is 4.11 AV each year.

seeing the quality of the conditions for viewing an astronomical object at the time of observation. Degrees of good or bad seeing depend upon the amount of turbulence and movement within the Earth's atmosphere at the time of observation. Sometimes a set of Roman numbers is assigned to "seeing" with I being extremely good through to V which is very bad.

seismology The study of seismic waves generated by earthquakes and movements within the surface of the Earth, Moon and other heavenly bodies. Such events, which may also include collisions or impact of one body on another, set up waves which travel through the body. Two types of wave are generated, S (or shear) waves and P (or compressional) waves. P waves travel faster than S waves and can move through liquids, gas or solids but S waves only move through solid structures such as rock. The study of these waves and their interactions with surrounding matter enables information to be gained about the nature of the body in question and the events which triggered them.

selenography The study of the geographical and topographical surface features of the Moon.

selenology The scientific and geological study of the Moon.

semiregular variables (SR variables) a class of vast, pulsating variable stars which have variations in brightness usually in the order of one to two magnitudes. These variations show a definite degree of pattern or periodicity, lasting anything from days to years, but are also subject to irregular non-predictable changes over time. The group has been further divided into four sub-groups: (1) SRa are RED GIANTS with fairly stable PERIODS. (2) SRb are red giants with irregular periods. (3) SRc are red SUPERGIANTS. (4) SRd are giant and supergiant stars of spectral types F, G and K, which are yellow with extreme luminosity. (*see* ANTARES, BETELGEUSE). Mu Cephei, known as the Garnet star due to its strong red colour, is a supergiant type and in the CONSTELLATION CEPHEUS of magnitude 3.6 to 5.1.

sensitivity the smallest signal that can be detected above background "noise" in recording equipment.

separation the angular distance, measured in arc seconds, between two stars in an optical double or visual BINARY STAR system.

Serpens (The Serpent) a CONSTELLATION which is unique in being split into two parts of different sizes. The largest part, Serpens Caput (The Serpent's Head) lies near Corona Borealis (The Northern Crown) in the northern hemisphere. The smaller part, Serpens Canda (The Serpent's Body) is sited in the southern hemisphere and partly within the MILKY WAY, near SCORPIUS. The two parts lie on either side of the constellation OPHIUCHUS (The Serpent Bearer). Serpens Caput contains a globular cluster, MS and many RR LYRAE stars. Serpens Canda contains a nebula, M16, known as the EAGLE NEBULA. There are nine bright stars over 4th magnitude in Serpens and the brightest of these is called Alpha Serpentis and is of 2nd magnitude.

Sextans (The Sextant) a faint and inconspicuous CONSTELLATION lying in the southern hemisphere near LEO. It has one brighter star of 4th magnitude.

Seyfert galaxy spiral a type of galaxy which was first described in 1943 by Carl Seyfert. The distinguishing feature of this type of galaxy is its extremely bright nucleus, a significant source of non-thermal radiation. Most of the emission is in the infrared and they are also sources of X-rays and ultraviolet, but weak at radio wavelengths. There are two groups of Seyfert galaxy (depending upon types of emission lines) and they may be a passing phase in the life of most spiral galaxies.

shadow bands a phenomenon which is sometimes observed if the sky is very clear, immediately before and after a total ECLIPSE of the sun. Narrow bands or patches of light and shadow move erratically over the Earth's surface but the reason for them is imperfectly understood. It is believed to involve irregular refraction of light from the thin crescent of the Sun, caused by particles in the Earth's atmosphere (*see* SCATTERING).

shell star a type of hot star, usually spectral type B of a particular kind, called Be. The spectrum of these stars is very complicated having deep, well-defined absorption lines, and, on either side wings of emission lines. These are all superimposed upon the normal broad absorption spectrum. There is thought to be a ring of material around the star, thrown off by the high speed of its rotation, which is the cause of the complex spectrum seen in this type of star.

shepherd satellites small moons or SATELLITES of a PLANET, which may occur in pairs, and exert a sufficiently great gravitational pull to keep particles in a ring around the planet. Examples are PANDORA and PROMETHEUS which hold the F ring of SATURN and ATLAS, which is the shepherd satellite for the planet's A ring.

short period comet a type of COMET which travels an elliptical orbit and appear to be held there by the gravitational pull of the PLANETS, particularly JUPITER. Short-period comets have PERIODS less than 200 years and are moving in the same direction as the planet by which they are held, (although HALLEY'S COMET is an exception to this).

sidereal day the period of time occupied by the rotation of the Earth with respect to the stars. It is the interval of time between two consecutive passages of the CATALOGUE equinox across a chosen meridian. It lasts for 23 hours 56 minutes and 4 seconds and is 3 minutes 56 seconds less than a solar day. 24 sidereal hours make up one sidereal day.

sidereal month The period of time taken for the Moon to orbit the Earth relative to a star or group of stars whose position is considered fixed. The sidereal month lasts for an average of 27.32166 days.

sidereal period the time taken by a moon or satellite, or planet to travel one orbit around its primary body, measured with respect to the stars.

sidereal rate The speed at which an EQUATORIALLY MOUNTED telescope must be driven around its polar axis, in order to keep it fixed upon one particular point in the sky allowing exactly for the rotation of the Earth. One complete revolution of the polar axis takes a SIDEREAL DAY.

sidereal time measured with respect to the rotation of the Earth in relation to the stars. The sidereal hour angle at any selected place determines the "local sidereal time" which is measured in SIDEREAL DAYS, hours, minutes and seconds.

sidereal year the period of time taken by the Earth to travel its orbit around the Sun, measured in relation to the stars.

singularity a mathematical theory which postulates a point or region where time and space become absolutely distorted and ordinary laws of physics no longer apply.

Sinope one of the small moons or SATELLITES of JUPITER which was first recorded in 1914 by S.B. Nicholson.

Sirius (The Dog Star; Alpha Canis Marjois; CMa) a brilliant VISUAL BINARY star with a magnitude -1.46 which is one of the closest to Earth at a distance of 8.7 light years. It lies in the CONSTELLATION CANIS MAJOR and the primary is an A STAR while the companion, Sirius B, is a

WHITE DWARF. The existence of Sirius B was first suspected in 1844 and it was detected by means of a more advanced telescope in 1862. However, it was not until the first quarter of this century, when its spectrum was taken, that it was recognized as a white dwarf, the first to be described as such, in 1925. Sirius has an orbital period of 50 years and is the brightest star after the Sun.

solar activity a collective term for various phenomena connected with the Sun that take place within a regular cycle but vary in frequency and magnitude. The average length of cycle of solar activity is about 11 years but longer cycles may occur. SUNSPOTS are one example of solar activity.

solar constant the sum total of the electromagnetic energy from the Sun, measured over the Earth's mean distance per unit time (currently 1.37kWm^{-2}).

In physics, it is the energy *received* on the Earth's surface, allowing for any losses due to the atmosphere.

solar cycle the cycle of SOLAR ACTIVITY, particularly relating to SUNSPOTS, which lasts for about eleven years.

solar spectrum the spectrum of the Sun extending from gamma ray to radio wavelengths. Some parts of the curve are considerably affected by the cycle of SOLAR ACTIVITY with great variations in intensity.

solar system the system comprising the Sun (a star of SPECTRAL TYPE G) around which are the nine planets in elliptical orbits. Nearest the Sun is MERCURY, then VENUS, EARTH, MARS, JUPITER, SATURN, URANUS, NEPTUNE, and PLUTO. In addition, there are numerous satellites, a few thousand (discovered) asteroids, and millions of comets. The age of the solar system is put at 4.5 to 4.6 billion years, a figure determined by the radiometric dating (uranium-lead) of IRON METEORITES. Iron meteorites are thought to be fragments of cores from early planets and thus representative of the early stages of the solar system.

solar units a means of describing the physical properties of a star or other body in relation to those of the Sun. Examples are solar mass, solar radius and solar luminosity.

solar wind the term for the stream of charged, high-energy particles (primarily ELECTRONS, PROTONS and alpha particles) emitted by the Sun. The particles travel at hundreds of kilometres per second, and the wind is greatest during flare and sunspot activity. Around the Earth, the particles have velocities of 300-500kms^{-1}, and some become trapped in the magnetic field to form the VAN ALLEN RADIATION BELT. However, some reach the upper atmosphere and move to the poles, producing the auroral displays (*see* AURORA).

solstices the time at which the SUN reaches its most extreme position north or south of the equator. There are two such instants in the year.

Sombrero galaxy (M104; NGC4594) A spiral GALAXY situated in the constellation Virgo, which is edge-on to Earth making its structure difficult to view. It has an extensive bright nucleus and a broad band of dark dust, giving an appearance of a hat with a wide brim.

spacetime a reference framework in which events can be placed and related in space and time. The concept is derived from the theory of relativity and the principle that the speed of light is constant and independent of the observer; it thus applies to any observer, from anywhere in the universe, irrespective of relative motions.

speckle interferometry a technique for measuring small angles, e.g., the diameter of stars, which utilizes the principle of interference of light.

spectral line a line of emission or absorption, occupying a narrow wavelength band in a SPECTRUM. Spectral lines occur when there is a change over between two levels of energy in an atom or ion. A change to a lower level releases a photon and this results in an emission line. A change to a higher level, with the "mopping up" of a photon, results in an absorption line.

spectral type a classification system for stars, based upon the SPECTRUM of light they emit. The sequence is, in order of descending temperature: O-hottest blue stars; B-hot blue stars; A-blue white stars; F-white stars; G-yellow stars; K-orange stars; M-coolest red stars. The system originates from Harvard College Observatory which originally had classes A to Q but this was altered and ordered by temperature to give the quoted classes which can be further subdivided into categories numbered 0 to 9. There are also more recent additions such as S stars and carbon stars. The temperature ranges are as follows:

type		
	O	>25 000K
	B	11 000 - 25 000K
	A	7500 - 11 000K
	F	6000 - 7500K
	G	5000 - 6000K
	K	3500 - 5000K
	M	<3500K

In addition, a number of descriptive letters are used as prefixes and suffixes to provide further information about the stars' spectra, including:

c	sharp lines
d	dwarf (main sequence star)
D	white dwarf

e	emission
ep	peculiar emission
g	giant
k	interstellarlines
m	strong metallic lines
n	diffuse lines
s	sharp lines
sd	subdwarf
wd	white dwarf
wk	weak lines

The luminosity of stars was also subdivided:

Ia	luminous supergiants
Ib	less luminous supergiants
II	bright giants
III	normal giants
IV	subgiants
V	dwarfs (main-sequence stars)

This enables any star to be classified readily.

spectrograph an instrument used in astronomy for separating and recording the component SPECTRAL LINES of radiation from celestial sources. They are used in conjunction with various types of telescope.

spectroheliogram an image of the Sun obtained using a SPECTROHELIOGRAPH.

spectroheliograph an instrument for photographing the Sun using a single wavelength of light (i.e., monochromatic light).

spectrometer the instrument used to observe and study a spectrum.

spectroscopic binary a BINARY STAR determined as such by the nature of its spectral lines. There are two types: double-lined comprising two spectra superimposed on each other but which are moved one relative to the other by the DOPPLER EFFECT, and single-lined which consist of two stars that differ only in luminosity. In this case the spectrum is that of the brighter star but differences in wavelength permit identification as a spectroscopic binary.

spectroscopy the generation, study and interpretation of spectra using spectroscopes (which includes spectrometers, spectrographs, etc.). The light emitted by a hot object, or given out by a substance upon excitation, can be analysed. Emission and absorption spectra (depending upon whether radiation is given out or taken in by the source) are specific to the ions, atoms and molecules producing them and their analysis can help identify components in stars, nebulae, atmospheres, etc. Additional information such as temperature, presence of magnetic fields, etc., can also be determined through spectroscopy.

spectrum (*plural* **spectra**) the separation of a beam of electromagnetic radiation into its constituent elements as defined by different wavelengths. The obvious example is splitting a beam of white light into its constituent colours by passing it through a prism. The natural equivalent is a rainbow. The full electromagnetic spectrum ranges from radio waves to gamma radiation and includes among others, visible light, microwaves and X-rays.

Spectra occur as *emission line, absorption line* or *continuous* and can occur together. Continuous emission or absorption occurs over a range of wavelengths and is produced by BLACK BODY RADIATION. Line spectra are caused by the absorption or emission of certain wavelengths by atoms or molecules.

speed of light as revealed in the theory of RELATIVITY is a universal and absolute value, independent of the speed of the observer. The value is 2.998 $10^8 ms^{-1}$ or 186,281 miles per second.

spherical aberration an imperfection in a lens or mirror in which light rays do not all converge at the same point because parts of the lens or mirror are at different distances from the optic axis and have different focal lengths. It occurs with spherical lenses and mirrors.

spicules short-lived features in the Sun's CHROMOSPHERE that last only a few minutes. They have a thin elongate form and measure approximately 1,000 kilometres across and 10,000 kilometres in length. They are gas jets with temperatures of 10,000 to 20,000K.

spin the angular momentum of an elementary particle or nucleus.

spiral galaxy a type of GALAXY that has spiral arms and which was classified by Hubble into two groups based upon the existence or absence of a central bar. These groups are further subdivided on morphology. The Milky Way is a typical spiral galaxy with stars and interstellar material in a disc and the arms. The spiral arms tend not to be fixed structures but reflect more the conglomeration of stars and other material in certain positions which orbit the galaxy centre.

s-process (*see also* R-PROCESS) a process of NUCLEOSYNTHESIS which in contrast to the r-process is slow. Light elements are converted into heavier ones through the capture of neutrons in a star, but the density of neutrons is low and the new nucleus undergoes beta decay (loss of an electron) before the capture of another neutron. This process is linked with the red giant phase of a star.

S star a red giant type of star which is similar to an M star but in place of prominent absorption bands for titanium oxide has bands for zirconium oxide. These stars also have a high carbon to oxygen ratio. These differences are due to effects of nuclear reaction in the depths of the star.

star a body of fiery gas, similar to the Sun, which is contained by its own gravitational field. Stars produce energy by thermonuclear reactions (NUCLEAR FUSION) and the core acts as a natural nuclear reactor where hydrogen is consumed to form helium with the production of electromagnetic radiation. A classification system groups stars as SPECTRAL TYPES and the stages in the life of a star are called STELLAR EVOLUTION (*see also* HERTZSPRUNG-RUSSELL DIAGRAM). The largest known stars have one hundred times the mass of the Sun. Stars consist primarily of hydrogen with helium (about 6% of atoms) and other elements being present in very minor amounts.

starburst galaxy a galaxy in which there is a very high rate of star formation occurring, with an associated and very high production of infrared radiation. Starburst galaxies differ from active galaxies in that the star formation occurs over a wide area and their wide distribution was only discovered in 1983 when a survey of infrared galaxies was undertaken by the Infrared Astronomical Satellite, IRAS.

star catalogue a database on stars providing observations and information concerning position, magnitude and related properties. One such catalogue is the AGK.

star cluster form two main types: GLOBULAR CLUSTERS and OPEN CLUSTERS and are groups of stars thought to have the same origin.

star formations *see* **stellar evolution**.

steady-state theory initially an alternative theory to that of the BIG BANG, but which now has little support. It assumed the universe was constant everywhere and that its continued expansion was balanced by the creation of matter. The theory was effectively disproved by the discovery of the cosmic microwave background and also radio source counts. Part of the theory supporting NUCLEOSYNTHESIS survives as this applies to either model.

stellar evolution the various stages of the life of a star, which begins with the creation of the star from the condensation of gas, primarily hydrogen. The growth of the clouds pulls in more gas, and the increase in gravity compresses the molecules together, which attracts more material and creates a denser mass. The heat normally produced by molecules due to their vibratory motion is increased greatly, and the temperature is raised to millions of degrees which facilitates NUCLEAR FUSION. The supply of hydrogen continues to be consumed (and the star occupies the MAIN SEQUENCE of the HERTZSPRUNG-RUSSELL DIAGRAM) until about 10 per cent has gone, and then the rate of combustion increases. This is accompanied by collapses in the core and an expansion of the hydrogen-burning surface layers, forming a RED GIANT. Progressive gravitational collapses and burning of the helium (generated by the consumption of the hydrogen) result in a WHITE DWARF, which is a sphere of enormously dense gas. The white dwarf cools over many millions of years and forms a black dwarf-an invisible ball of gases in space. Other sequences of events may occur, depending upon the size of the star formed. BLACK HOLES and NEUTRON STARS may form from red (super) giants via a SUPERNOVA stage.

stellar mass the mass of a star which is frequently quoted as a number of solar masses—M_o. It is an important parameter upon which depend many other stellar properties and its evolution.

stellar populations *see* **Populations I, II and III.**

stellar wind an outpouring of matter from a hot star which is particularly large for red giants and ultraviolet stars, where the winds flow at vast speeds. Stellar winds are discernible in cool supergiant stars, but the velocities are considerably lower.

stony-iron meteorite a meteorite comprising metallic and stony components. There are two major types, *pallasites* (grains of the magnesium silicate mineral olivine surrounded by metal) and *mesosiderites*, which are mixtures of metal (nickel-iron) and silicate minerals.

stony meteorites meteorites composed mainly of rock-forming silicates, including pyroxene, olivine and plagioclase with some nickel-iron. This type accounts for the vast majority of meteorites that are *seen* to fall. They are termed either chondrites or achondrites, depending upon the presence, or lack, of chondrules, which are glassy droplets up to 2mm in size, produced by the melting and sudden cooling of silicate material.

stratosphere the layer of the atmosphere above the TROPOSPHERE, which stretches from 10 to 50km (6 to 31 miles) above the ground. It is a stable layer with the TROPOPAUSE at the base. The temperature increases from the lower part to the upper, where it is 0°C, and the higher temperatures are due to ozone-absorbing ultraviolet radiation. The inversion of temperatures creates the stability that tends to limit the vertical extent of cloud, producing the lateral extension of, for example, cumulonimbus cloud into the anvil head shape.

Strömgren sphere the spherical envelope to a hot star of type O or B that contains ionized gas, mainly hydrogen with helium.

S-type asteroid an asteroid type common in the inner asteroid belt. They are thought to contain silicates and could be the precursors of STONY METEORITES.

subdwarf a smaller and fainter star which forms a band below those in the MAIN SEQUENCE on the HERTZSPRUNG-RUSSELL DIAGRAM. They are POPULATION II stars of the older halo type and are primarily of type F, G or K. Their position is due to a lower content of the heavier metals.

subgiant a giant star that lies between the main sequence and the giants on the HERTZSPRUNG-RUSSELL DIAGRAM. Subgiants are smaller and less luminous than giants of the same spectral type.

submillimetre-wave astronomy astronomy that involves the study of electromagnetic radiation with a wavelength of 0.3 to 1 millimetre. It uses a combination of techniques from infrared and radio astronomy and to avoid the disruptive effects of atmospheric water vapour, the telescopes must be sited at dry, high places. It is an important branch of astronomy in the study of star formation, interstellar clouds and the cosmic microwave background.

Sun the star nearest to Earth and around which Earth and the other planets rotate in elliptical orbits. It is a star of average size and brightness and is a dwarf of SPECTRAL TYPE G2 on the MAIN SEQUENCE. Its diameter is $1.392 \ 10^6$ kilometres and its mass approximately $2 \ 10^{30}$ kilograms.

Energy is generated from nuclear fusion in the core where the temperature is roughly 15 millionK. The surface temperature is about 6,000K although this falls to nearer 4,000K at the top of the PHOTOSPHERE. It is made up mainly of hydrogen (70% by mass) and helium, with 1 or 2% of heavy elements (anything heavier than hydrogen and helium),

Beyond the core is the *radiative* (or *radiation*) *zone* and then the *convection* zone in which gas currents flow up, releasing energy at the surface. These currents are responsible for the mottling or *granulation* of the Sun. The surface layer, the photosphere, is the source of visible light and origin of solar activity and is overlain by the CHROMOSPHERE, which is pierced by SPICULES and PROMINENCES. The outermost layer is the CORONA.

sungrazer a comet that passes through the Sun's outer layers (CORONA). There is a small group of such comets which tend to be very bright.

sunspots the appearance of dark areas on the surface of the SUN. The occurrence reaches a maximum approximately every eleven years in a phase known as the sunspot cycle. They are usually short-lived (less than one month) and are caused by magnetism drawing away heat to leave a cooler area which is the sunspot. The black appearance is due to a lowering of the temperature to about 4,000K. Sunspots have intense magnetic fields and are associated with magnetic storms and effects such as the *aurora borealis* (*see* AURORA). They may send out solar flares which are explosions occurring in the vicinity of the sunspots.

supercluster structures that are hundreds of millions of light years across and which consist of a grouping of several clusters of galaxies. They contain about ten or twelve rich galaxy clusters and each supercluster is growing. About fifty are known.

supergiant one of the largest and most luminous star types which may be up to five hundred times larger than the Sun and thousands of times more luminous. They are relatively rare, examples including Betelgeuse in Orion and Antares in Scorpius, and potentially may become SUPERNOVAE.

supernova (*plural* **supernovae**) a large star that explodes, it is thought, because its hydrogen supply is exhausted whereupon it collapses producing high temperatures and triggering thermonuclear reactions. The energy released is so vast that a supernova can be brighter than the Sun by a factor of 100 million. An even greater amount of energy is expended on ejected material on still further energy in released NEUTRINOS.

There are two basic types of supernova, Type I and Type II. They are distinguished by their spectra and Type I supernovae are further divided on spectral evidence. The collapse of the core actually happens in under one second and when the density has increased to a certain point the pressure wave is reversed and the outer layers of the star explode to leave a neutron star at the core. Supernovae are rare. The most recent was in 1987 in the Large Magellanic Cloud and this was the first that could be seen unaided since 1604.

supernova remnant the material blown out of an expanding star at the time of a SUPERNOVA. Remnants tend to be strong x-ray and radio sources.

surge a solar PROMINENCE occurring as an ejection of material from the chromosphere into the CORONA in a spiked form. They are relatively short-lived (10 to 20 minutes) but may reach heights of two hundred thousand kilometres.

symbiotic stars a variable star that shows spectral features of both a cool star (e.g., an M type at 3,500K) and hot gases at 20,000 from a B star. It is interpreted as a close binary comprising a low temperature RED GIANT with a companion WHITE DWARF, with gas streaming from the former onto the latter.

synchronous rotation also called **captured rotation** is when a satellite has the same face toward the parent planet due to a coincidence of rotation and orbit. This phenomenon applies to the Moon although LIBRATION causes some deviation.

synchrotron radiation electromagnetic radiation given out when ELECTRONS with very high energy pass thorough a magnetic field almost at the speed of light. This radiation was first noticed in experimental physics, using synchrotron accelerators, hence the name. It is thought to be the primary source of emission from radio sources such as RADIO GALAXIES and SUPERNOVA REMNANTS. Synchrotron radiation is easy to identify spectrally and X-rays and light from the Crab Nebula are produced in this way due to electrons from the central PULSAR.

T

tail *see* **comet.**

Taurus (The Bull) one of the ZODIAC CONSTELLATIONS described by Ptolemy in AD 140 which is extensive and conspicuous. It is situated near ORION and partly within the MILKY WAY in the northern hemisphere. It contains some very bright stars, the brightest being Aldebaran which is zero magnitude and Elnath, first magnitude. It contains the HYADES and PLEIADES CLUSTERS and also the CRAB NEBULA. The prototype T. TAURI and RV TAURI stars lie within the constellation Taurus.

Taurus A the RADIO SOURCE belonging to the CRAB NEBULA within the CONSTELLATION TAURUS.

tekites small, often rounded pieces of natural glass which are found in four regions of the world in vast areas called strewn fields. They have a high silica content of 70 to 80% and contain about 11 to 15% aluminium, and are in the region of 0.75 to 65 million years old. They are thought to have been made by the impact of giant METEORITES which caused the melting and fusion of terrestrial rock.

telescope an instrument for magnifying an image of a distant object. The main astronomical types are *refractors* and *reflectors*. The refracting type have lenses to produce an enlarged, upside-down image. In the reflecting type, there are large mirrors with a curved profile which collect the light and direct it onto a second mirror and into the eyepiece.

Telesto a small moon or satellite of the planet SATURN which was discovered in 1980 and has an irregular outline. It has a co-orbit with two other satellites, Calypso and Tethys.

terminator the boundary between the hemisphere of a planet or moon which is lit up by the sun, and that which is facing away and lies in darkness. Due to the rotation of the heavenly body, there is a sunrise and a sunset terminator, and its appearance is governed by surface features and the presence or absence of an ATMOSPHERE.

Tethys a moon or satellite of the planet SATURN which was first discovered in 1684 by Giovanni Cassini. It has a very low density, suggesting that a large proportion of its composition is ice, and it has a diameter of 1,050 kilometres. There are many craters covering the surface, the majority with diameters ranging in size from 25 to 50 kilometres. However, one enormous crater, Odysseus, has a diameter of 400 kilometres. The presence of these craters shows that Tethys has been subjected to collision and bombardment from material travelling at high speeds. The most notable and unique feature of Tethys is the presence of a gigantic canyon or chasm, Ithaca Chasma, which extends three quarters of the way around the satellite from near the north pole towards the south pole. It is 2,000km long, 100km wide and 4 or 5km deep.

Thalassa a small moon or satellite of the planet NEPTUNE which was discovered by the Voyager 2 space probe in 1989.

Thebe a small moon or satellite of the planet JUPITER, which has an irregular outline and was discovered in 1979 by S.P. Synnott.

thermal radiation electromagnetic radiation resulting from the high temperature of a body. The radiation is emitted as a result of interactions between molecules, atoms and electrons, usually ionized gas, in a dense, hot state. (Compare NON-THERMAL RADIATION; *see also* BLACK BODY RADIATION.)

tide tides affect the surface layers of a planet (or natural satellite) whether liquid or solid, due to the effects of gravitational forces. The ocean tide on Earth is due mainly to the attraction of the Moon, but also the Sun. Variation in tides is caused by the positions of the three bodies and when the Moon and Sun pull in the same direction, there is a high spring tide; when they are at right angles there is a low neap tide. Other factors that affect tides are the uneven distribution of water on the Earth's surface and the topography of the sea bed.

time zone a geographical area or band of the Earth's surface throughout which civil time is the same. The areas are bands of longitude 15° wide and there is a one hour time difference between adjacent bands. However, the boundaries of the bands are irregular to take account of the distribution of land and centres of population. In some places the time difference is half an hour rather than one hour.

Titan the largest moon or satellite of the planet SATURN, which was discovered in 1655 by Christiaan Huygens. The only satellite larger than Titan in the SOLAR SYSTEM is JUPITER'S GANYMEDE. Titan has a diameter of 5,150 kilometres and it takes nearly 16 days to travel its orbit around Saturn, a distance in the region of 1,222,000 kilometres. It is a reddish orange colour due to photochemical reactions within its thick, foggy atmosphere. This atmosphere is composed almost entirely of molecular nitrogen, but methane, carbon dioxide, carbon monoxide, acetylene, cyanoacetylene, methylacetylene, diacetylene, cyanogen, hydrogen cyanide, ethane and propane are present in minute amounts. At the surface, the pressure exerted by this thick atmosphere is 1.6 times greater than that of the Earth. It is believed that methane may play a similar part in Titan's atmosphere to water in Earth's. It may variously exist as a solid, liquid or gas, possibly with methane rain falling onto the satellite's surface. The surface temperature on Titan is in the region of -178°C and its density is 1.88g cm^{-3}. It is thought that it is composed half of rock and half of ice with methane lakes on its surface. More information about the nature of Titan is expected to be gained from the Cassini/Huygens space probes which will be launched in 1997 and reach Saturn in 2004.

Titannia the largest moon or satellite of the planet URANUS which was discovered in 1787 by William Herschel and has a diameter in the order of 1,550 kilometres. It is thought to be composed of a mixture of rock and ice and has an icy surface with a low ALBEDO. The Voyager 2 probe which took photographs of Titannia in 1986, revealed that the surface of the satellite was covered with craters. Many are of small size but a few larger ones occur such as the Gertrude basin which has a diameter in excess of 200 kilometres. Also, there are numerous faults (fractures caused by movements in the rocks) which may be as much as 5 kilometres deep, some of which dissect the craters. One of the largest is called MESSINA CHASMA which extends for about 1,500 kilometres.

Titius-Bode Law A mathematical law which enables the approximate distances of the planets from the sun to be predicted. It is arrived at by taking the sequence 0, 3, 6, 12, 24, 48 etc. and adding 4 to each and dividing by 10. This then gives the sequence 0.4, 0.7, 1.0, 1.6, 2.8, 5.2 which corresponds well with the real distances measured in astronomical units (AU). The formula works well for the seven inner planets and if the ASTEROIDS are included together at 2.8 AU. However, it fails to correctly describe the distances for Neptune and Pluto. The law was formulated by Johann Titius in 1766 and published in 1772 by Johann Bode, and is usually known as "Bode's Law". At that time, the existence of the asteroids was unknown. Astronomers realised that there was a gap at 2.8 AU and predicted that there was a small planet there. This was later discovered to be largest of the asteroids, CERES.

topocentric co-ordinates the co-ordinates of a heavenly body when measured from the Earth's surface, as compared to geocentric co-ordinates, which are adjusted so that they can be considered to have been measured from the Earth's centre.

Transient Lunar Phenomenon (TLP) passing and short-lived changes in the appearance of some surface features on the Moon, such as coloured patches or glows, or obscuring of the detail of features. These may be linked with lunar tides and particularly seen to occur within some of the Moon's craters (Gassendi, Aristarchus and Alphonsus) or basins, but their significance remains obscure.

transit (1) the passage of either the planet MERCURY or VENUS (called the "inferior planets") across the disc of the sun (2) the passage of a heavenly body such as a star, as it travels its daily path, across the MERIDIAN of an observer (3) the passage of a moon or satellite across the disc or face of its planet.

transit circle also known as the meridian circle, this is the circle made by an optical telescope which is fixed so that it can only swing in a vertical north-south plane. Transit

circles enable very accurate measurements to be made of
the positions of the heavenly bodies as they pass across
the MERIDIAN of the telescope.

Trapezium an open cluster of very young stars, dust and gas
lying in the ORION NEBULA, the name being conferred by the
four most prominent ones which make up the multiple star
called Theta Orionis. These are of magnitudes 5.1, 6.7, 6.7
and 8.0 and can be seen with the aid of a small telescope.
These stars form a hot and dense cluster which ionize and
illuminate the ORION NEBULA.

Triangulum (the Triangle) a small but prominent
CONSTELLATION lying in the northern hemisphere which is
situated near to PERSEUS and between ARIES and
ANDROMEDA. It was first described and listed in AD 140 by
Ptolemy and has three bright stars of 3rd magnitude which
form a triangle. A large spiral galaxy, M33, lies within the
Triangulum Constellation.

Triangulum Australe (The Southern Triangle) a small but
prominent CONSTELLATION lying in the southern
hemisphere, partly within the MILKY WAY and near CRUX. It
contains three very bright stars which form a triangle, the
brightest being Atria, an orange GIANT of magnitude 1.9.
The other two, Beta and Gamma are of magnitude 2.9.
This constellation was first depicted in an atlas published
in 1603 by Johann Bayer.

Triangulum Galaxy (M33; NGC 598) a spiral galaxy
situated within the TRIANGULUM CONSTELLATION which is the
third largest member of the LOCAL GROUP and is at a
distance of 2.7 million light years. It lies face on to Earth
and its spiral arms contain numerous young stars.

Trifid nebula (M20; NGC 6514) an EMISSION NEBULA
situated in the CONSTELLATION SAGITTARIUS which is a huge
cloud of ionized hydrogen. The nebula gains its name by

its apparent division into three parts by dark dust bands extending from the centre.

triple-alpha process a nuclear fusion reaction which occurs in the interior of a star once all the hydrogen in the core has been used up and the temperature has climbed to 100 million degrees. Hence it occurs only within evolved stars and involves the fusion of three helium nuclei, (also known as ALPHA PARTICLES). Carbon is formed and gamma ray energy released. The reaction, also called the Salpeter process, is defined by the formula: $3^4He^{12}C + g$.

Triton the largest moon or satellite of the planet NEPTUNE which was first seen in 1846 by William Lassell, just after the discovery of Neptune itself. It has several unusual features, one of which being its retrograde orbit around the planet. It takes Triton nearly 6 days to complete its orbit around Neptune, and it is tilted at an angle of 23. It is gradually moving down in spiral fashion towards the surface of Neptune and in about 100 million years will approach the ROCHE LIMIT. The Voyager 2 space probe obtained valuable photographic observations of Triton in 1989. It is extremely cold, the coldest known body in the SOLAR SYSTEM, with a surface temperature of 37K, and the icy crust is believed to surround a dense core of rock and possibly metal. At the south pole there is a cap of pinkish coloured nitrogen ice and snow which is slowly evaporating. Triton has a very thin atmosphere, most of which is composed of nitrogen but methane and carbon monoxide are present in small amounts. It has a diameter of 2,700 kilometres (1,680 miles) and a highly complicated surface of craters and large cracks. Volcanic activity, indicated by geysers of nitrogen, which erupt from the surface to a height of about 8km, show that complex surface movements are still taking place.

Trojan Group in fact, two groups of ASTEROIDS which share the ORBIT of the planet JUPITER around the Sun. Each group is collected near one of the two LAGRANGIAN POINTS 60 on either side of Jupiter and are held there. Each Trojan Group, Jupiter and the Sun lie at three points of an equilateral triangle. There is considerable oscillation and alteration in position of individual members of the groups, and possible collisions between them may cause the number of asteroids to change over a period of time. The first to be discovered, in 1906, was named Achilles, and subsequent ones have all been called after participants in the Trojan Wars. They are all extremely dark but it is believed that as many as 1,000 (as yet mainly un-named), may be sufficiently bright to be visible from Earth.

troposphere the Earth's atmosphere between the surface and the tropopause (the boundary with the stratosphere). This layer contains most of the water vapour in the atmosphere and most of the aerosols in suspension. The temperature decreases with height at approximately 6.5°C per kilometre, and it is in this layer that most weather features occur.

T Tauri star a type of very young star or PROTOSTAR that has just condensed out of the INTERSTELLAR MEDIUM, and is rapidly throwing off material and contracting. T Tauri stars have strong emission lines in their spectra and are of spectral type G. They are often found in loose groupings, known as T Tauri associations, and almost always occur in dark clouds of dust and gas. T Tauri stars vary irregularly, thought to be due to changes in the CHROMOSPHERE related to speed of rotation, and absorption of the light by dust clouds. T Tauri stars are believed to be the youngest type of those which have a mass about the same as the Sun. (Other larger types are known as AE and BE stars). The presence of large amounts of lithium, which is usually lost at an early stage in a star's evolution, is one indication of the extreme youth of T Tauri stars. They have surface temperatures in the region of 3,500 to 7,000K and many are rotating very fast and throwing off matter at high speeds up to 300kms⁻¹. The prototype, T Tauri, lies within the CONSTELLATION of TAURUS, but many stars of this type are now known.

T Tauri wind a rapid outflowing of material from a T TAURI STAR, resembling a SOLAR WIND but with a much greater loss of matter. The material travels at hundreds of kilometres per second and is sometimes in the form of a bi-polar, two-lobed stream.

T type asteroid an ASTEROID belonging to a class which has a very low ALBEDO.

Tucana (The Toucan) a CONSTELLATION in the southern hemisphere which was first depicted in 1603 in the star atlas of Johann Bayer. It lies near GRUS (The Crane) and contains the small MAGELLANIC CLOUD. It has two bright stars of 2nd and 3rd magnitude, the 3rd one Beta being a double star. The constellation also contains a bright and extensive GLOBULAR CLUSTER called 47 Tucanae (NGC 104) which is of 4th magnitude and easy to view from Earth.

Tully-Fisher relation a method of determining the distances of remote SPIRAL GALAXIES which was devised in 1977 by B. Tully and R. Fisher. The technique uses the relation between a spiral galaxy's absolute photographic magnitude and the speed of its rotation.

Tunguska event an enormous and violet explosion which took place in the Tunguska region of Siberia on June 30th 1908. It caused devastation over a wide area, and sound and shock waves which reverberated around the world. The event is believed to have been caused by the

explosion of a meteorite, comet nucleus or asteroid at a
height of 8.5km above the Earth's surface. No remains of
the object, or crater, have ever been found suggesting that
it totally disintegrated. The energy of the explosion (5 x
10^{16} joules) caused the widespread devastation on Earth
although fortunately, there was no loss of life.

twilight a period after sunset and before sunrise when the
sky is partially lit up by scattered light rays from the sun.
"Civil twilight" is the interval of time when the zenith
distance of the centre of the disc of the sun is between
9050 and 96. "Nautical twilight " is the period between 96
and 102 and "astronomical twilight" the interval between
102 and 108.

twinkling *see* **scintillation.**

Tycho's star a SUPERNOVA of type I, situated in the
CONSTELLATION CASSIOPEIA, which was first seen in 1572
and carefully studied by Tycho Brae. It is a source of X-
rays and radio waves.

U

ultraviolet astronomy the observation and recording of electromagnetic radiation from stellar or other sources, which lies in the wavelength band range of 91.2 to 320 nanometres. At one end of the scale there is a transition between "extreme ultraviolet" and the X-ray band, starting at about 6 to 60 nanometres. This is called XUV and it merges into extreme ultraviolet (EUV) which lies in the wavelength band range, 10 to 100 nanometres. The range 100 to 200 nanometres is called the Far Ultraviolet (FUV), and 200 to 320 nanometres is the Near Ultraviolet (NUV). The Earth's atmosphere absorbs most of the radiation in the ultraviolet range hence high altitude balloons, rockets or satellites are required for observations. The spectral lines of many important chemical elements (both atoms and molecules) lie within the UV wavelength band. Hence ultraviolet astronomy provides very important and significant information.

umbra (1) a dark inner area of total shadow within which the source of light is not visible, as in a total solar ECLIPSE. The PENUMBRA is the outer portion of the shadow, within which the light source is partially visible. (2) The dark inner part of a SUNSPOT where the magnetic field is most intense and strong and vertical, which is cooler than the surrounding penumbra.

Umbriel a moon or satellite of the planet URANUS which was first observed by W. Lassell in 1851. The Voyager 2 space probe, which approached Uranus in 1986, took photographs of Umbriel which showed that it was much darker than the planet's other satellites. Numerous craters cover the surface which are believed to be of fairly recent origin. One of these is 110km in diameter and is called Skyund. Its centre is occupied by a high bright peak which makes it a distinctive feature compared to the rest of the surrounding darkened surface.

universal time a precise measurement of time, designated UT, which is related very closely to the mean daily movement of the Sun. It forms the universal basis of all civil timekeeping and is defined by a mathematical formula which relates it to SIDEREAL time. This is derived from direct observations of the stars and depends upon the position of the observer, and is called UTO. The timescale obtained by correcting UTO, independent of the point of observation (necessary because of irregular and variable POLAR MOTION), is called UT1. Co-ordinated universal time or UTC is the time given by broadcast time signals, and is based on International Atomic Time (TAI) but differs from it by the insertion or deletion of "leap seconds" when necessary. UTC is kept within + or - 0.90 seconds of UT1.

universe the sum total of all that exists or entirety of objects which may, potentially be known.

Uranus the seventh planet in the SOLAR SYSTEM and one of the four *gas giants* with an orbit between those of Saturn and Neptune. Uranus has a diameter at the equator of 50.080 kilometres and lies an average distance of 2869.6 million kilomtres from the Sun. The surface temperatures are in the region of -240°C. It is composed mainly of gases with a thick atmosphere of methane, helium and hydrogen. Uranus was the first planet to be observed with a telescope and was discovered by William Herschel, a German astronomer in 1781. Uranus remained a mystery until quite recently, but in 1986 Voyager 2 approached close to the planet and obtained valuable information and photographs. The planet appeared blue, due to its thick atmosphere of gases and a faint ring system of 13 main rings was seen. Uranus was known to have five moons but a further ten, some less than 50 kilometres in diameter, were discovered.

A day on Uranus lasts for about 17.5 hours and a year is equivalent to 84 Earth years. Its largest moon is TITANIA with a diameter of 1600 kilometres. All five moons are very cold and icy with a surface covered in craters and cracks. ARIEL has deep wide valleys ad MIRANDA, the smallest moon, is a mass of canyons and cracks with cliffs reaching up to 20 kilometres. Uranus has a greatly tilted axis so that some parts of the planet's surface are exposed to the Sun for half of the planet's orbit (about 40 years) and are then in continuous darkness for the rest of the time. Due to the tilt of the axis, the Sun is sometimes shining almost directly onto each of Uranus' poles during parts of its orbit.

Ursa Major (The Great Bear) a CONSTELLATION in the northern hemisphere which is one of the most familiar and easily recognized. It was described in AD 140 by Ptolemy and is extensive and readily apparent having nineteen stars brighter than fourth magnitude. The three brightest stars (magnitude in the order of 1.8) are called Alcaid, Alioth and Dubhe. Seven main stars in Ursa Major form the Plough, and two of these, Dubhe and Merak, are in line with the Pole Star (POLARIS) and are called POINTERS. A group of galaxies within the constellation, including the spiral M81 and M82, belong to the LOCAL SUPER-CLUSTER. One of these, M82, is also a STARBURST GALAXY.

Ursa Minor (The Little Bear) a constellation in the northern hemisphere, described by Ptolemy in AD 140, and containing the north CELESTIAL POLE. POLARIS, or the present pole star, is the brightest one in the constellation and is of second magnitude. It lies within on degree of the north celestial pole. One other star of second magnitude is called Kochab and is an orange SUBGIANT.

V

Van Allen belts two belts of radiation consisting of charged particles (electrons and protons) trapped in the Earth's magnetic field. They were discovered in 1958 by the American physicist James Van Allen. The lower belt occurs between 2000 and 5000 kilometres above the equator and its particles are derived from the Earth's atmosphere. The particles in the upper belt, at around 20,000 kilometres, are derived from the solar wind. The Van Allen belts are part of the Earth's magnetosphere, area of space in which charged particles are affected by the Earth's magnetic field rather than that of the Sun.

variable star a star with physical properties which vary over the course of time, both on a regular and irregular basis. The most obvious variation is in brightness and a graph which plots the brightness of a star against time is known as a light curve. The period of one cycle in brightness on the light curve may last minutes or years, and may be regular or irregular. For any particular variable star, the magnitude of brightness may show a broad range. The reasons why variation occurs fall into three categories. They may arise from changes within the physical state of the star (intrinsic variables), factors or processes outside of the star (extrinsic variables), or as a combination of both. *See also* CATACLYSMIC VARIABLE, ECLIPSING BINARY, PULSATING STAR.

Vega also known as Alpha Lyrae or μ Lyr, is an A STAR which is the fifth brightest in the sky. It is an easily recognized white star which is the brightest one in the constellation Lyra, having a MAGNITUDE of 0.03.

Vela (The Sail) this is a CONSTELLATION in the southern hemisphere situated partly within the MILKY WAY and earlier identified in the 1700s as one of the parts of a much larger constellation, Argo Navis (The Ship). It lies near the Southern Cross (CRUX) and is sometimes confused with it, as some of its component stars form a false cross (*see* ASTERISM). One of its brightest stars, Gamma, which is a multiple star is a rare WOLF-RAYET type. This constellation contains the VELA PULSAR.

Vela pulsar a young PULSAR, about 10,000 years old, occurring in the constellation VELA. It emits pulses of radio emission in a short period of 89 milliseconds (0.089 seconds) and also gamma rays. In 1977 it was discovered to be an optical pulsar, resembling that in the CRAB NEBULA although much weaker, and also similar in being associated with the remnant of a SUPERNOVA. In common with other pulsars its rotation rate is slowing down and it is losing energy. Several temporary surges or increases in rotation rate (known as glitches), have been noticed since recordings of the pulsar first began. However, in general the PERIOD is increasing by about 10.7 nanoseconds each day.

Venus the second planet in the SOLAR SYSTEM with its orbit between those of Mercury and Earth, and it is also the brightest. It is known as the Morning or Evening star. Venus is about 108.2 million kilometres (67 million miles) from the Sun and is extremely hot with a surface temperature inthe region of 470°C. It has a thick atmosphere of mainly carbon dioxide, sulphuric acid and other poisonous substances which obscure its surface. The size of Venus is similar to Earth with a diameter at the equator of 12,300 kilometres. The atmosphere of carbon dioxide traps heat from the Sun (the greenhouse effect) allowing none to escape. Hence the surface rocks are boiling hot and winds whip through the atmosphere at speeds in excess of 320 km/hr. Venus is unusual in being the only planet to spin on its axis in the opposite direction to the path of its orbit. Also it spins very slowly so that a "day" on Venus is very long, equivalent to 243 Earth days. A year is 225 days. Venus has no satellites and because its surface is hidden, much of the known information about the planet has been obtained from space probes. The *Magellan* space probe launched by the USA in 1989 visited Venus, sending back valuable photographs. Venera 13, a Russian probe landed on Venus in 1982, and obtained a rock sample and other information. The surface of the planet has been shown to be mountainous with peaks 12 kilometres high. It is covered with craters and also a rift vally. It is possible that there are active volcanoes.

Vesta (Asteroid 4) the third largest known ASTEROID and the fourth to be discovered, in the early 1800s, by H. W. M. Olbers. It is the only asteroid to be sometimes bright enough to be detected by the naked eye. It occasionally reaches a visual magnitude of 6 and can be seen when conditions for observation are at their most favourable. Its brightness in due to a high ALBEDO of 0.23 which is greater than that of any other large asteroid. Its diameter is in the region of 501 kilometres and it is thought to have a surface of basalt, resembling METEORITES of the EUCRITE type. Its surface is not uniform, as is indicated by changes in spectrum and colour when it rotates. One rotation lasts for 5.43 hours and Vesta has a mass in the order of 3×10^{20} kilograms.

Virgo (The Virgin) one of the ZODIAC CONSTELLATIONS which is very large and extensive containing a cluster of faint GALAXIES known as the VIRGO CLUSTER. It contains one bright star of 1st MAGNITUDE called Spica and several others of 2nd and 3rd Magnitude, and is the second largest constellation.

Virgo A a very strong source of radio emission associated with a large, elliptical GALAXY designated M87 in the VIRGO CLUSTER. M87, which is an enormous galaxy, has a JET emerging from its centre and there is thought to be a supermassive BLACK HOLE within the core. The galaxy is believed to have an enormous mass of over 10^{13} solar masses.

Virgo Cluster a vast CLUSTER of about 2,500 GALAXIES in the CONSTELLATION VIRGO, three quarters of which are SPIRAL, a few are irregular and the rest elliptical in shape. The M87 galaxy is a source of both radio and X-ray emissions (*see* VIRGO A). Another large galaxy within the cluster, M86, which is also elliptical in shape, is another source of X-rays. The Virgo cluster lies at the centre of the LOCAL SUPERCLUSTER (*see also* LOCAL GROUP).

visual binary a BINARY STAR in which the two members are far enough apart to be visible separately when viewed with an appropriate telescope, or even with the naked eye. Usually, one partner is brighter than the other and this is called the primary star, while the dimmer one is termed the companion. Usually, visual binaries have very long ORBITAL PERIODS, sometimes so long that it is not possible to distinguish any orbital motion. These appear to remain together as they travel across the sky and are called common proper motion stars. Examples of visual binaries are Gamma Centauri and Sirius.

Volans (The Flying Fish) a small faint CONSTELLATION in the southern hemisphere situated near the LARGE MEGELLANIC CLOUD. It was first described in the early 1600s and was named Piscis Volans, by Johann Bayer. Of its six main stars some are 3rd and the rest 4th MAGNITUDE.

V-type asteroid a class of ASTEROID represented by only one known example, VESTA.

VV Cephei star a class of gigantic BINARY STARS of which there are few known examples, but those which have been studied include VV Cephei, KQ Puppis and AZ Cassiopeiae. The primary star is an enormous SUPERGIANT usually of SPECTRAL TYPE M (see M STAR) but sometimes G (See G STAR). The companion is a hot blue B star and mass is transferred to this from the supergiant. These stars have very irregular orbits and are a more evolved form of a type of ECLIPSING BINARY STAR called Zeta Aurigae.

W

wavelength the shortest distance between two points of the same phase on a wave of radiation. It is given the symbol and is the distance travelled during one cycle of oscillation, e.g., the distance between two crests or troughs. It is measured in metres.

whirlpool galaxy a galaxy given the number M51; NGC 5194 which was first described in 1845 by Lord Rosse. It is a SPIRAL GALAXY, face-on to us (type Sc in the HUBBLE CLASSIFICATION) and has a smaller, irregular, companion galaxy (number NGC 5195) connected to one of its spiral arms. It lies at a distance of 13 million light years from the Earth in the constellation of Canes Venatia.

white dwarf a type of star that is very dense with a low luminosity. White dwarfs result from the explosion of stars that have used up their available hydrogen. Due to their small size, their surface temperatures are high, and they appear white (*see also* SUPERNOVA).

Wolf-Rayet star one of a class of rare, extremely luminous and exceptionally hot stars with temperatures on the surface in the order of 20,000 to 50,000K and perhaps as great as 90,000K. They are characterized by broad and strong emission lines of ionized oxygen, carbon, helium and nitrogen but absorption lines are few. They were discovered in 1867 by C. J. E. Wolf and G. Rayet and two subgroups are now recognized, WC stars and WN stars. In the WC subgroup, the emission lines are mainly of carbon, helium, and oxygen, whereas in the WE type they are of nitrogen and helium. A further WO type in which there are strong oxygen emission lines, has recently been discovered. All these types have a low amount of hydrogen, and about half these stars are known to be of a BINARY type. All these stars are believed to be rapidly losing mass through a stellar atmosphere which is expanding extremely fast at speeds in the order of 3,000km s^{-1}. These high speed stellar winds are rapidly stripping the Wolf Rayet stars of their mass, and the material can sometimes be seen as surrounding ring nebulae. The reasons and mechanisms to account for the loss of mass of Wolf Rayet stars in not fully understood.

Wolf sunspot number (R) an indication of the amount of sunspot activity on the solar disc derived from the formula $R = k(10g + f)$. In this, k is a constant depending upon equipment used and the observer, g is the number of sunspot groups and f the total number of their component spots. The Wolf number was introduced in 1848 by Rudolf Wolf working in Zurich. He used old data to extend the record of activity back to the 1750's. It has now been superseded by the International Sunspot number (RI).

X

X-ray astronomy stars emit a variety of electromagnetic radiation including X-rays, but this is unable to penetrate the Earth's atmosphere to be detected. Very hot stars send out large amounts of X-rays which can be detected by equipment contained on space satellites. The satellite ROSAT launched in 1990 has equipment to undertake X-ray astronomy and obtain information about distant bodies in space (e.g. WHITE DWARFS and SUPERNOVAE) that are emitting X-rays.

X-ray binary the most common source of bright galactic X-rays, derived from BINARY STARS, in which one of the pair is a degenerate star such as a WHITE DWARF, BLACK HOLE, or NEUTRON STAR. Gas is transferred from the non-degenerate star to its degenerate partner, and during this process, gravitational energy results in a heating of the material to temperatures great enough for X-rays to be emitted.

X-ray burster a source of cosmic X-rays, characterized by intense bursts of activity of a random nature. They were first discovered in 1975-6 and have a rapid onset often repeating at intervals of a few seconds to one minute. Two types have been recognized: Type One which repeat every few hours or days and Type Two which repeat more rapidly over a period of a few days. It is believed that the source is an X-ray BINARY in which the degenerate partner is a NEUTRON STAR. The material being transferred is believed to be helium and when the NEUTRON STAR has accumulated or accreted a certain amount of material, a critical point of temperature and pressure is reached, which results in a thermonuclear explosion.

X-rays the type of high energy radiation lying between gamma rays and ultraviolet in the ELECTROMAGNETIC SPECTRUM. The magnitude of energy varies and the wavelength of X-rays is in the range of 12 to 0.012 nanometres. Low energy X-rays are called soft, and high energy X-rays hard. Gas at very high temperatures produces thermal X-rays, whereas non-thermal X-rays result from the interaction of high energy electrons in a magnetic field (SYNCHOTRON EMISSION). Or, low energy photons may collide with high energy electrons to produce non thermal X-rays as in the Compton effect. Galactic sources give rise to both thermal and non thermal X-rays.

Y

year the amount of time taken for the Earth to complete its orbit around the sun, which is determined by the reference point selected (*see* CALENDAR).

YY Orionis star one of a number of variable stars which may be a subclass of T TAURI stars. Alternatively, they may be stars at an earlier stage of development and they are characterized by an emission line with absorption towards the red side.

Z

Zeeman effect an effect which is noticed when atoms in a magnetic field give off or absorb radiation. It has the effect of splitting a spectral line into two, or several components which remain close together, as the magnetic field alters the configuration of the atoms. Sometimes, the spectral line appears blurred and broader, and individual components cannot be detected. The Zeeman effect is used to study the strength of the magnetic field of various heavenly bodies such as the Sun and stars, as indicated by the degree of spacing of the components.

zenith a point which lies directly above an observer on the CELESTIAL SPHERE and is vertically overhead. The geocentric zenith is a line from the centre of the Earth through the point where the observer is standing, to a point of the CELESTIAL SPHERE. It is usually not the same as the zenith because the Earth is not a true sphere.

zodiac a band of twelve CONSTELLATIONS, originally named by the ancient Greeks and called the signs of the zodiac, which includes the annual path (the ECLIPTIC) apparently travelled by the Sun when viewed from the Earth. The zodiacal constellations are Aries, Taurus, Gemini, Cancer, Leo, Virgo, Libra, Scorpius, Sagittarius, Capricornus, Aquarius and Pisces, and originally the ecliptic only passed through these. However, PRECESSION has since caused an eastward shift of the zodiacal constellations by more than 30°, and the ecliptic now passes through a thirteenth called Ophiuchus.

ZZ Ceti star one of a number of pulsating, variable WHITE DWARF stars resembling the one after which they are named, ZZ Ceti. The surface temperature of these stars is in the region of 12,000K with PERIODS between 30 seconds and 30 minutes. The variation in luminosity in ZZ Ceti stars is in the order of 0.05 to 0.3 MAGNITUDE.